After  historical romances because it combines her love of a happy ending with her passion for history. She lives in Christchurch, New Zealand, but spends her days immersed in the world of late Victorian England.

Beguiling the Duke
is Eva Shepherd's gripping debut
for Mills & Boon Historical!

Discover more at millsandboon.co.uk.

BEGUILING
THE DUKE

Eva Shepherd

MILLS & BOON

First Published in Great Britain 2019
by Mills & Boon, an imprint of HarperCollins*Publishers*
1 London Bridge Street, London, SE1 9GF

© 2019 Eva Shepherd

ISBN: 978-0-263-26938-3

MIX
Paper from
responsible sources
FSC™ C007454

This book is produced from independently certified FSC™ paper
to ensure responsible forest management.
For more information visit www.harpercollins.co.uk/green.

Printed and bound in Spain
by CPI, Barcelona

To Julia Williams, Bryony Green
and the editorial team at Harlequin, for their support,
guidance and encouragement.

Chapter One

London 1893

Rosie Smith raised the delicate bone china cup to her lips, took a sip of the fragrant Darjeeling tea and sighed with contentment.

Despite being a penniless orphan, with no prospects worth mentioning, here she was, dressed in the latest fashion, taking tea at the Ritz, surrounded by Britain's elite.

Her feet, encased in soft kid leather boots, were aching after spending all day walking around the shops and sights of London. She was still tired from the gruelling trip across the Atlantic from New York. And yet she couldn't be happier.

She sighed again and looked across the lace-covered table at her friend, who was smiling with equal contentment.

'What shall we do tomorrow?' Rosie took a

cucumber sandwich from the top layer of the three-tiered cake stand and placed it on her rose-patterned plate. 'More shopping? Or shall we take in some art galleries and museums?'

'Art galleries and museums, I think.' Arabella placed a scone on her plate and smothered it with jam and clotted cream. 'After all, I'm sure Father would want us to absorb as much culture as we can while we're in England.'

The two girls giggled conspiratorially.

Rosie lifted a finger and waggled it in Arabella's direction. '"What good is art, my dear? You don't get a decent return on sculptures. Nobody ever got rich from culture."'

Arabella clapped her hands and laughed loudly. 'You do such a brilliant impersonation of Father. It's you who should be on the stage, Rosie, not me.'

Their jubilation drew the attention of the women sitting at the next table, who glared down their imperious noses with looks that might have withered the spring buds on the tree. Rosie was tempted to poke out her tongue. Instead she lifted her head and returned their looks of disapproval. Although she suspected being glared at down a small button nose wouldn't have quite the same impact.

'Humourless old biddies,' she whispered. 'Have they never heard anyone laugh before?'

She smiled at Arabella. 'So, tomorrow it's art galleries and museums—perfect.'

The two girls sipped their tea and sighed simultaneously.

A waiter approached the table and bowed low. Arabella smiled her thanks, removed the folded letter from his silver tray and read its contents. Her smile dissolved. Her hand shot to her mouth and her shoulders slumped.

'What is it? What's wrong, Bella?' Rosie reached across the table and touched her friend's arm.

Arabella's hands trembled as she passed her the letter. Rosie quickly scanned the elegant handwriting. It was an invitation from the Dowager Duchess of Knightsbrook, inviting Arabella to a weekend party at her estate in Devon.

'Oh, this is too, *too* terrible, Rosie.' Arabella took a lace handkerchief from her embroidered clutch purse and dabbed at her eyes. 'It's from the mother of that horrid man Father expects me to marry.'

'It's disgusting!' Rosie threw the letter down on the table. 'They think they can buy you. That all they have to do is dangle a title and you'll come running, and then they can get their greedy hands on your father's money. Disgusting!'

'I know... I know. I don't want to go. And I especially don't want to go that weekend. It means

I'll miss the opening night of Oscar Wilde's play. I'll miss the opportunity to meet the great man himself.'

'Then don't go.' Rosie thumped the table, making the teacups jump and rattle in their saucers. 'You can't possibly miss the opening of that play. That's one of the main reasons we came to England.'

Her raised voice drew another scowl from the next table. This time Rosie didn't hold back. She screwed up her face, poked out her tongue and let the women know just what she thought of their disapproving looks.

Their gasps and bulging stares would have made Rosie laugh if she had felt like laughing.

Arabella lowered her handkerchief. 'Well, no…the main reason we're here is because Father wants to marry me off after that…' She tilted her head and lightly bit her upper lip. 'After that scandal.'

'Scandal? That was no scandal. Your appearance on the New York stage as Lady Macbeth was a triumph and should be celebrated as such. Your father just doesn't understand your passion for acting.'

Arabella sent her friend a shaky smile. 'Thank you, Rosie. But I'll still have to go, Father will never forgive me otherwise.

'And I'd never forgive myself if you missed that play. There *has* to be a way out of this.'

Rosie drummed her fingers on the table and looked around the room for inspiration. There had to be a way out of this dilemma; there was always a way out of every problem.

'I'll go instead.' She smiled in triumph.

Arabella twisted her handkerchief in her lap. 'You'll what?'

'I'll go in your place. The Dowager and the Duke have never met me. If I tell them I'm Arabella van Haven how will they ever know the difference? We've both got black hair and blue eyes, and everyone always says we look like sisters. They'll see a fashionably dressed young woman, and all they'll be thinking about is getting their hands on your father's money. They'll never suspect I'm not you.'

'Oh, Rosie, you can't… Can you?'

'Of course I can.'

Arabella screwed her handkerchief into a tighter ball. 'But, Rosie, you might get caught.'

'Nonsense. It's a perfect plan. And when has one of my plans ever gone wrong?'

Arabella frowned in concentration. 'Well, there was that time you said Cook wouldn't notice the missing cakes if we moved those remaining around the pantry. And there was the time you said that if we dressed as boys and went to the local fair we'd be able to get work on the side-shows. And then there was that time you were certain that if we told our tutor we knew everything there was to know about—'

Rosie held up her hand to stop the flow of words. 'Those were mere childish pranks. This time it's serious—and, really, what choice do we have? You don't want to go to this party, do you?'

Arabella shook her head.

'You don't want to miss the play's opening, do you? You don't want to marry this Duke, do you? You don't want to end up living out in the countryside, miles away from the nearest theatre, do you?'

Arabella shook her head more emphatically.

'Right, then leave it to me. You said it yourself. I'm almost as good an actress as you.' She stabbed her finger at the abandoned letter. 'This horrid Duke of Knightsbrook will be completely fooled.'

'Well, I suppose you *could* pretend to be me...' Arabella chewed her lip again, as if not wholly convinced.

'Of course I can. And I'll have fun doing it. This stuffy Duke will think he's wooing the wealthy, beautiful Arabella van Haven. Instead he'll be wasting his energies pursuing a penniless, plain, charmless ward. And it will serve him right.'

'You might be penniless, Rosie, but no one

could ever describe you as plain or charmless. You're beautiful, kind, funny and the best friend I could ever—'

Rosie held up her hand again, to stop Arabella's praises. 'Whether that's true or not, I can't say—but I certainly won't be appearing charming in front of the Duke. After all, it might be your father's wish that you marry a titled man, but that's not what *you* want, is it?'

Arabella straightened her spine. 'It certainly is not.'

'So I'm going to have to convince this stuffy Duke that the last thing he wants to do is marry the appallingly behaved and completely unacceptable Arabella van Haven, despite her father's fortune.'

Arabella smiled and placed her handkerchief back in her purse. 'You're so clever, Rosie.' She paused, her purse half closed. 'Except…'

'Except what?'

'I've just thought of a big flaw in your plan. Aunt Prudence was going to accompany me as my chaperon.'

Rosie rolled her eyes. 'Aunt Prudence is too sick to go anywhere. Or at least she thinks she is. I suspect she won't be over her imagined seasickness until it's time to go back to New York.'

Arabella covered her mouth to stifle a giggle. 'Poor Aunt Prudence—she *is* a bit of a hypochondriac. But you can't go without a chaperon. They'd get suspicious if a young unmarried woman of twenty arrived at their estate unaccompanied.'

Rosie would not be deterred. 'Then I'll take Nellie. I'll need a lady's maid anyway, and Nellie enjoys a good caper as much as we do. When I tell her we're doing it so we can make sport of a family of greedy aristocrats there'll be no stopping her. Nellie will be the perfect chaperon.'

'This is *so* good of you, Rosie. You're always so kind to me.'

Rosie waved her hand in front of her face to dismiss the compliment. Arabella's happiness meant everything to her.

Rosie drew in a deep breath and ran her hand down the soft pink silk of her stylish gown. Arabella had saved her from a life of poverty and loneliness. Without her, Rosie couldn't imagine how hard her life might have been. She closed her eyes and shuddered. But she was not alone any more. Thanks to Arabella she had not been forced to try and survive on the streets of New York with no money and without a friend.

There was nothing she wouldn't do for the friend who had saved her from such a life. And she hated to see Arabella sad.

Her friend had been so kind to her, had always

treated her as an equal, and she had such little happiness in her life. Rosie saw it as her job to keep her friend happy, so she might be distracted from the neglect she felt over her father's constant absences.

Spending the weekend with a stuffy aristocratic family to save her from an unwanted marriage was nothing compared to the enormous debt she owed her friend. And at least poverty had one compensation. While Arabella's father was determined to marry her off to a titled man for his own social advancement, he had no such concerns when it came to Rosie. Nobody, including Rosie herself, expected anyone to want to marry a penniless orphan who didn't even own the clothes she was wearing.

She smiled and pushed away her unpleasant thoughts. What was the point of dwelling on such things? Today was all that mattered. Having fun was all that mattered. Not what had happened in the past, and not what the future might bring.

'Honestly, Bella. I want to do this. I'll get to have fun putting a stuffy duke in his place, and you'll get to see the play. And when I return I'll be able to regale you with tales of my exploits. It's perfect.'

Rosie smiled. She picked up a smoked salmon sandwich and placed it on her plate.

'Oh, yes, the Duke of Knightsbrook is going to regret ever thinking he can buy Arabella van Haven.'

Alexander FitzRoy, Lord Ashton, Eighth Duke of Knightsbrook, stifled a yawn and gazed over at the ormolu clock ticking on the marble mantelpiece. His mother, the Dowager Duchess, was in full voice, enumerating the seemingly exhaustive list of fine qualities that Arabella van Haven allegedly possessed.

'And I hear she's also accomplished on the banjo, and can recite large passages of Shakespeare from memory.'

His mother looked up at him with wide-eyed expectation. It seemed she had finally run out of accomplishments with which to tempt him.

Alexander uncrossed his legs and stretched. 'That's as may be, Mother, but I still have no intention of marrying the girl—no matter how many tunes she's capable of strumming on the banjo, or how many Shakespearean sonnets she can rattle off.'

'Don't be so hasty, Alexander. I know she's American, and that her father's a *banker*, of all things.' The Dowager grimaced. 'But they are minor drawbacks that I'm sure we can overlook. We need to focus on her finer qualities and not think about her background. After all, she is known for her beauty, and I've heard she possesses exquisite taste in—'

'Surely you have forgotten to list her most attractive attribute?' he interrupted, before his mother could start on another interminable list.

She cocked her head and smiled. 'And what would that be?'

'Her money.'

The Dowager spluttered, gripped the black lace at her neckline and sent him her sternest look. 'Don't be vulgar, Alexander. You're talking like a common tradesman.'

'Vulgar or otherwise, isn't that what this is all about? She has it—we don't. You want me to marry her and give her a title in exchange for her father's money.'

His mother's pursed lips drew into a thin line and her nostrils flared. It was an expression Alexander was familiar with—the one she had when she heard something she didn't like.

'You don't need to put it so crudely, but you can't deny it would solve all our problems.'

That was indeed something Alexander could *not* deny. The American heiress's money would solve their immediate financial needs, but it was a solution he would not demean himself even to consider.

His grandfather and his father had brought the once wealthy Knightsbrook estate to the brink of financial ruin, but their problems ran deeper than the merely financial. He could almost forgive them squandering excessive amounts of money on gambling, partying and women. *Almost*. But what he could not forgive was them bringing the family's once noble name into total disrepute.

He intended to restore the family's fortune by hard work and modernisation. He also intended to restore the family's tarnished name—and that would not be achieved by selling the title Duchess of Knightsbrook to the highest bidder.

'You're right, Mother. Her father's money *would* provide a short-term solution to our money problems.'

The Dowager smiled and rose from her chaise longue.

'But it would be only that. A short-term solution. What is required is a long-term plan of action.'

The Dowager sank back onto her seat and sighed. 'Really, Alexander, sometimes you can be so tedious. Why don't you just marry the girl and be done with it?'

'Because if the estate is to return to its former glory we need to modernise. We're on the brink of the twentieth century and we're still using farming methods from the eighteenth century. That has to change.'

The Dowager flicked open her fan and waved

it rapidly in front of her face. 'Not this again. You and your plans to modernise will be the death of me. If you marry the American you won't have to worry about silly steam trains and traction engines. I want to look out on people using scythes to bring in the harvest—not horrible pieces of wheezing and coughing machinery.'

'That's as may be, Mother, but I'm sure the tenants would rather live on a prosperous estate, where their homes and livelihoods are protected, than in poverty in what *you* see as a picturesque setting.'

'Oh, pish-posh.' The Dowager waved her fan more rapidly. 'Anyway, you're twenty-eight now. It's time you married. You shouldn't let that unfortunate incident with Lydia Beaufort put you off marriage for ever.'

Alexander clenched his jaw so tightly it began to ache. *Unfortunate incident.* Was that how his mother described something that had all but devastated him?

He inhaled deeply to release the tension gripping his neck and shoulders. 'Lydia Beaufort has nothing to do with me not wanting to marry the American. And that, Mother, is my final word on the subject.'

It might be his final word, but he knew from experience it would not be his mother's.

She frowned her disapproval and looked

around the room, as if seeking further support for her argument. She spotted Charlotte, sitting quietly in the corner reading a book.

'What about your sister?'

Charlotte looked up. 'What *about* me?'

'Well, you're going to need a husband soon. Heaven only knows no man is going to want to marry a girl who reads as much as you do and is always getting involved in these ridiculous social causes unless she comes with a decent dowry. Your brother wouldn't be so selfish as to deny you the happiness of marriage.'

Charlotte slammed shut her book. 'For your information, I have no intention of—'

Alexander shook his head slightly, giving his younger sister a silent signal that now was not the time to fight that particular battle with their mother.

Charlotte scowled at her mother and forcefully opened her book again, breaking the spine. She frowned at what she had done, and then went back to reading.

'I will make sure Charlotte is well provided for,' Alexander said.

'Yes, and you can make sure she is well provided for by marrying Arabella van Haven.'

Alexander shook his head and sighed audibly.

'Anyway,' the Dowager continued, undeterred. 'It's all arranged. I've invited her to a house party this weekend. You'll be able to discover for yourself just how ideal a bride she will make and how lucky the man will be who marries her.'

Alexander sprang to his feet. 'You've done *what*?'

'Oh, sit down, Alexander, and don't glare at me like that. I've invited her for the weekend. It will give you a chance to get to know her.'

'Mother, haven't I told you often enough that we need to economise? We cannot afford to host lavish parties.'

The Dowager flicked her fan at him. 'It's just a small house party—nothing too elaborate. And you can see it as an investment in the future. Isn't that what you're always going on about? Well, meeting Miss van Haven will be an investment in your future.'

She sent him a victorious smile.

'Putting aside the complete lack of logic in your argument, you've invited her here under false pretences. I won't lie to her. I will make it clear at the first opportunity that I will not be marrying her.'

'Oh, you and that overblown sense of honesty. You were just as bad when you were a boy, but I would have thought you'd have grown out of it by now.'

'Would you prefer it if I told lies, the way Father and Grandfather did?'

The way Lydia Beaufort did.

His mother's lips tightened, but she made no reply.

'Our family has lost just about everything. Surely you don't expect me to lose my belief in the importance of honesty as well? And if Arabella van Haven is as virtuous as you say she is then I'm sure she will also believe in the value of honesty and will want to know the truth.'

'Oh, yes, I've heard she *does* value honesty in all things. I've also heard she's modest, gentle, demure, and temperate in all areas. And they say that she…'

Alexander sat down and sighed as his mother went back to listing the litany of virtues possessed by the apparently saintly Arabella van Haven.

It seemed his mother would not be stopped in her plan to make her the next Duchess of Knightsbrook, and he was going to have to endure the company of the title-seeking heiress for the weekend. But eventually his mother and the American would both realise his mind was made up, and Arabella van Haven would have to pursue some other duke, earl or marquess desperate for American dollars—because the position of his wife was not for sale.

Chapter Two

❧

It was magnificent. Simply magnificent.

Rosie stood just inside the entrance of Knights-brook House and looked up at the ornate domed window in the ceiling, shedding a soft light over the two-storey entrance hall. She tried to settle her breathing as she took in the opulence and grandeur of it all.

The coach trip through the estate's parklands had been no less spectacular, with its seemingly endless parade of trees festooned with spring foliage. When the trees had cleared and she'd first seen the expansive four-storey house standing proudly beside a large lake, dominating the landscape around it, her resolve had faltered. Arabella's father was a man of immense wealth, but this was something more than just wealth. The house seemed to proclaim that here was the home of one of England's oldest and noblest families—one that was reverently referred to as 'old money'.

Rosie inhaled slowly and deeply. She would not be overawed by her surroundings. Nor would she be daunted by the stern looks of the ancestors staring down at her from the oil paintings that lined the walls of the expansive hall. Arabella's happiness depended on her keeping her nerve.

She just had to remember who these people really were. They were a stuffy aristocratic family who had fallen on hard times. They were people so arrogant that they thought all they had to do was dangle a title in front of a rich American and then they could continue to live in splendour, despite having lost all their own money.

Well, they were about to find out that not all Americans were quite so easily bought. They needed to be taught a lesson, and she was just the woman to do it.

A man and a woman appeared at the top of the grand staircase and began the long descent.

'That must be them, the rascals.' Nellie scowled beside her. 'Go teach them a lesson, Rosie.'

Rosie tried to calm her breathing and stifle her fluttering nerves. She just had to remember that she was no longer poor Rosie Smith. She was Arabella van Haven, daughter of a wealthy and influential banker. And she was a young woman whose tendency to misbehave in polite society made her a decidedly unsuitable bride for a member of the aristocracy.

'Right…' She gave Nellie a pointed look. 'It's time for Arabella to put on a show.'

Rosie spread out her arms wide, smiled and started twirling. Round and round she went, faster and faster, down the length of the entrance hall, her satin skirt spreading out around her in a pale blue circle.

The black and white marble floor tiles merged into one swirling mass. Priceless Chinese urns whooshed past her face. She whirled past statues, past the paintings of the ancestors, all the while emitting a loud *whoo-whee* noise. Dizzier and dizzier, she kept spinning—until she reached the bottom of the staircase.

Stopping abruptly, she looked up to see what impact her entrance had made. The room continued to spin, twirling in front of her eyes as if she were locked inside a child's spinning top.

She reached out, tried to grasp something—anything to stop the room from moving. With both hands she clasped the thin stand of a nearby pedestal, clinging to it as if her life depended on it. The Chinese vase sitting on top of the pedestal wobbled. It tilted. It began to fall.

Rosie let out a loud squeal and dived forward to catch the delicate vase before it crashed to the floor. Her hands gripped the vase. Her feet slid out from beneath her and she tumbled forward.

Before she hit the floor strong hands had surrounded her waist, lifted her up and set her back on her unsteady feet.

Still clasping the vase, Rosie closed her eyes briefly, to try and halt her spinning head and still her pounding heart. She opened them and stared into the eyes of her rescuer. Then closed them again immediately.

It couldn't be.

This astonishingly handsome man could *not* be the stuffy Lord Ashton.

Rosie opened her eyes and blinked a few times, but his appearance became no less stunning.

While he had the haughty, reserved demeanour she had come to expect from the British aristocracy, he had the symmetrical good looks, chiselled cheekbones and full sensual lips she had seen on statues of Greek athletes at the British Museum.

He also had that air of masculine vitality those Greek sculptors had captured so well in their subjects.

Rosie looked down at the floor and gulped, remembering another anatomical feature the sculptures of naked Greek athletes possessed. But she most certainly would not think of that now.

Instead she looked back up and focused on how his dark brown hair brushed the edge of his high collar, and how, unlike most Englishmen she had met, his olive skin was clean-shaven.

And, unlike those Greek statues she wasn't thinking about, he was appropriately attired in a tailored grey three-piece suit, with a silver and grey brocade waistcoat.

Rosie coughed to clear her throat. 'Hello, I'm Arabella van Haven,' she said, hoping she didn't sound as foolish as she felt as she bobbed a curtsey, still clutching the vase to her chest.

He gave a formal bow and reached out his hands. Rosie stared at those long fingers, at the crisp white cuffs of his shirt contrasting with his skin, then looked up into his eyes. Brown eyes… so dark they seemed to absorb all light…eyes that were staring down at her, their accompanying black eyebrows raised in question.

'May I?'

'Oh, yes, of course.' She thrust the tightly clasped vase in his direction.

His fingers lightly touched hers as he removed the vase from her grip, setting off a decidedly unfamiliar reaction in her body. Her hands tingled and burned, as if she had held them too close to the fire. A strange sensation raced up her arm, across her chest, hitting her in the heart, causing it to pound in a wild, untamed manner.

He replaced the vase on its pedestal and turned back to face her. Her head continued to spin, her heart continued to dance—but surely that had nothing to do with his touch or his stunning good looks. It had to be due entirely to her whirling entrance.

'Miss van Haven, allow me to introduce myself. I'm Alexander FitzRoy, Duke of Knightsbrook, and may I present my mother, the Dowager Duchess of Knightsbrook?'

Rosie bobbed another curtsey, inhaled a quick breath and turned to face his silver-haired mother, who was wearing the strangest expression she had ever seen.

While Lord Ashton was giving every appearance of being unaffected by her unusual entrance, the same could not be said of his mother. Her contorted mouth was presumably meant to be smiling, but a frown kept taking over, causing her lips to twist and turn as if pulled by a puppet master's invisible strings.

It seemed she might have to work a bit harder to shock Lord Ashton, but the Dowager was going to be easy prey.

It was time to have some fun.

'Pleased to meet you, Your Grace.' She reached down, grabbed the Dowager's hand and pumped it in a manly handshake.

Those invisible strings gave her mouth a firm tug. The frown won, and the Dowager's nostrils flared as if she could smell something unpleasant.

Rosie bit the inside of her upper lip to stop herself from laughing as the Dowager finally forced her lips into a smile, her face contorting as if she were undergoing a painful dental procedure.

'I am pleased to make your acquaintance, Miss van Haven,' the Dowager replied, trying discreetly to rub the hand that Rosie had just crushed.

Rosie controlled the giggle bubbling up inside her. 'I'm really sorry about nearly breaking your vase—but it looks like it's a really old one, so perhaps it wouldn't have mattered.'

All three turned and looked at the offending porcelain ornament, now safely restored to its pedestal.

'Yes, it is rather old…' The Dowager sniffed. 'Ming Dynasty, I believe.'

A small giggle escaped Rosie's lips before she had a chance to stop it. 'Oh, as old as that? Well, then, it wouldn't have mattered if I'd broken it. It would have given you a good excuse to replace it with something nice and new.'

The Dowager's eyes grew wide, her tight lips compressed further, and she signalled to a footman to remove the vase, as if concerned that Rosie was about to commit a wanton act of vandalism.

They waited in silence as the footman gently picked up the vase and carried it reverently away in his gloved hands. When he'd safely left the room the Dowager exhaled slowly.

'I'm afraid you've arrived a little earlier than we were expecting, Miss van Haven. We usually greet our guests formally at the entrance,' the Dowager said.

'Oh, I like to take people by surprise. You never know what mischievous acts you'll catch them in.' Rosie winked at the Dowager and received a wide-eyed look of disapproval in response.

'Yes, quite…' she said, flustered.

Rosie looked over at the Duke, hoping to see an equally disapproving look. Instead he stared back at her with unflinching dark eyes, neither smiling nor frowning. Rosie's grin died on her lips and heat rushed to her cheeks.

What was happening? She *never* blushed. And she shouldn't be blushing now. She had to remain in character if she was to convince this man that she was a most unsuitable duchess. Just because he was sublimely handsome it did not mean she should let him unnerve her. She had to remember who he was and what he wanted to do. He wanted to marry Arabella to get his hands on her father's money.

'I imagine there's been a lot of mischief in these halls,' she said, trying to keep her voice light-hearted to disguise the disquiet the Duke was arousing deep inside her. 'I'm sure those ancestors could tell a tale or two.' She threw her arms up in the air and gestured wildly to the paintings lining the wall.

The Dowager took a step back to avoid Rosie's flying arms, while the Duke continued to stare down at her, his face implacable. She lowered her arms. It seemed that bad behaviour wasn't going to upset his demeanour. She would have to try another means of attack.

'Judging by all those portraits, your family has been wealthy for many generations. I suppose you realise that my father was born in poverty? His father was a miner, and his father's father was a mule driver.'

Let's see how the snobby aristocrats react to that!

The Duke nodded slowly. 'Yes, your father's history is well-documented. And he is to be commended for rising so quickly from such humble beginnings to become one of the wealthiest men in America. He's obviously an enterprising man and clearly believes in hard work.'

Rosie fought not to grimace. Was *nothing* going to annoy this man? Surely he couldn't be that rare entity, a member of the British aristocracy who wasn't a snob? Or was he just blinded by the thought of Arabella's substantial dowry?

'You're right. He does believe in hard work—in earning money rather than expecting a hand-out.'

Hopefully this Duke wouldn't be able to miss

her thinly veiled disapproval at his plans to marry Arabella for her money.

'Another thoroughly commendable trait.'

Damn. Either he didn't understand that he had just been insulted, or he didn't care.

'It's a shame your father couldn't accompany you this weekend,' the Dowager said. 'I was looking forward to meeting him in person.'

'No, he's too busy back in America.'

Making the money you're so desperate for.

'But meeting me is just like meeting him. I'm a chip off the old block, as they say.'

'Do they? How delightful…' the Dowager said through pinched lips.

Rosie supressed a smile at the Dowager's discomfort. A seed of doubt had definitely been planted in her mind after Rosie's entrance and behaviour. Now all she had to do was water that seed with continued bad behaviour and watch it grow until the FitzRoys realised they couldn't possibly countenance this marriage and sent her on her way.

Alexander almost felt sorry for his mother. This peculiar American woman was most definitely not what she had expected—of that there could be no doubt. But it seemed the thought of Mr van Haven's vast fortune was enough for her to swallow her astonishment and put on a brave face.

With forced politeness his mother led Miss van Haven back down the entrance hall she had just danced up, pausing at each painting and explaining which ancestor it depicted and what great exploit each was famous for.

It was fortunate for his mother that paintings of his father and his grandfather did not adorn the hall. He suspected even *she* would have had trouble finding anything with which to commend those two reprobates, and Miss van Haven's term 'mischievous' was far too tame to describe the damage that those two men had done to the family and to the estate.

Following the two women, Alexander had the opportunity to observe this odd American. His mother had been right about one thing: she certainly was attractive. With her raven-black hair and sparkling blue eyes she was nothing less than radiant. Nor could he deny that her creamy skin with the hint of blush on her cheeks gave her a delicate beauty. And that slightly upturned nose was rather appealing.

His mother was possibly right that she could play the banjo and recite long passages of Shakespeare—although he had no desire to discover whether either of those claims were true or not. But he suspected that nothing else about this young woman was what his mother had hoped for in a future daughter-in-law.

As his mother continued her boastful mono-
logue Miss van Haven nodded furiously, perhaps
unaware that her hat had become dislodged as
she had flung herself down the hall. It was now
sitting at a precarious angle, causing her to look
like a very pretty pantomime clown.

Alexander suspected a clown was also not what
his mother had had in mind for the next Duchess
of Knightsbrook.

Despite her feigned politeness, his mother
couldn't stop herself from shooting nervous
glances in Miss van Haven's direction. She was
no doubt worried that the young lady would suddenly break into a polka, trip over one of the
Queen Anne chairs, or send some other priceless
antique flying.

There was no question that her performance
had certainly been unexpected—but it was quite
obviously just that: a performance. While her
grandfather might have been a miner, and his father a mule driver, *she* had been raised among
America's wealthiest elite. The rules of etiquette
and manners were just as strict in New York society as they were in England. And men like her
father, who were newly wealthy, tended to follow
those rules even more rigidly than those who had
been born to wealth.

Miss van Haven had no doubt been given in-
structions from a very young age on the cor-

rect way to behave in every situation—and that wouldn't have involved insulting her hosts by acting in such an outrageous manner.

Why she felt the need to behave in such a way Alexander could not fathom. Perhaps she felt her father's wealth meant she did not have to abide by even the most basic principles of politeness. But, whatever the reason, he had more pressing issues to deal with than the bad behaviour of a frivolous American heiress.

The sooner he could tell Miss van Haven that she would not be the next Duchess of Knightsbrook the sooner they could end this tedious ritual and he could get back to his work of transforming the family estate into a productive, financially viable farm.

She turned and looked in his direction and he realised he had been staring at her. Despite himself, he held her gaze, unable to look away from those stunning blue eyes. The colour was so intense—like a cool lake on a warm afternoon. And, also like a lake, they seemed to contain hidden depths—as if there was a deep, unfathomable sadness behind all her game-playing.

Her excessive grin faltered slightly, and a blush tinged her cheeks before she turned her attention back to his mother and once again resumed her frantic nodding.

They reached the front door, where her maid was still standing, her arms crossed defiantly.

'Now that I've introduced you to our family's history, perhaps Alexander will escort you round the gardens while I attend to my other guests? Your maid can be your chaperon.'

The maid folded her arms more tightly, shot Miss van Haven a questioning look, and received a quick nod in reply. Alexander wondered at the silent exchange, which seemed more like one between equals than maid and mistress.

His mother nodded to Arabella, sent Alexander a stern look—which was no doubt an admonition to do his best to charm the heiress—and then departed.

Alexander suppressed a huff of irritation. Escorting this title-seeking American around the estate was not exactly how he had intended to spend the day, but at least it would give him an opportunity to set her straight. To let her know that she would *not* be the next Duchess of Knightsbrook.

Chapter Three

Alone with the Duke—well, alone apart from Nellie—Rosie knew she had to keep her guard up. She could not let him see how much he unnerved her. She had to keep reminding herself that he was after Arabella's money. That was all that mattered.

She sent him what she hoped was a confident smile and got a familiar stern look in return.

'If I am to escort you round the gardens, can I make one request?'

She shook her head slightly. 'A request?'

'Yes—would you please stop this charade?'

One hand shot to her stomach; the other covered her mouth to stop a gasp from escaping. This was a disaster. He could *see* it was all an act. He *knew* she wasn't Arabella. Her plan was ruined before it had begun.

She looked out through the glass doors to the gardens. Could she escape? No, that was ridiculous. She was in the middle of the Devon countryside, many miles from London. What was she going to do? Walk? All the way back to the train station?

No, she was going to have to bluff her way out of this.

She scanned the entrance hall. Her mind spun with half-formed excuses and explanations.

'Charade?' she squeaked.

'Yes—this play-acting. You may have been able to shock my mother but it won't work on me, Miss van Haven.'

Rosie released the breath she'd been holding and slowly lowered her hand from her mouth. He didn't know she wasn't Arabella. All was not lost.

'Oh, yes. I'm sorry about that…' She gestured around the entrance hall, her hand twirling in imitation of her entrance. 'Just my little joke.'

His dark eyebrows drew together. He frowned slightly. 'Really? Are you in the habit of making fun of your hosts?'

'No, I…' She stopped.

Why make excuses? After all, she didn't *want* Lord Ashton to like her. She had to be completely unlikable if she was to convince him just what a thoroughly unacceptable duchess she would make.

'Well, yes. I do it all the time. I love making fun of people. Don't you?'

His frown deepened. 'No, I don't. Everyone deserves to be treated with respect, no matter who they are.'

Momentarily chastened, Rosie was tempted to agree with him—but she couldn't. The one thing she did not want was to be was agreeable.

'I guess we just see things completely differently. I think everyone is here for my entertainment and I like to have as much fun as possible. If people get offended and think I'm laughing at them—well, that's hardly my fault. Is it?'

He stared at her for a moment longer, as if observing a strange animal on display at the zoological gardens. 'I'm afraid I can't answer that.'

The response was vague, but Rosie could read his intent in his rigid body language. She had her wish. The Duke disapproved of her.

'Well, don't you worry if you don't know the answer. I'm sometimes not that smart either.'

'I don't doubt that, Miss van Haven.'

Rosie smiled. That almost sounded like an insult.

He offered her his arm. 'Mother would like me to show you the gardens. Shall we...?'

She placed her hand on his forearm and resisted the temptation to give the muscles a little squeeze, just to see how they compared to a marble statue.

They walked out through double French doors,

down some sweeping stone stairs and into the gardens, which looked just as magnificent at ground level as it had when she had driven through it in the carriage, with an abundance of trees, lush grasslands and a stunning lake adorned with ornate fountains.

As they strolled along a tree-lined pathway the soft green spring leaves rustled in the light breeze and small birds chirped and flitted between the branches. Rosie breathed in deeply and savoured the fresh country air. She had loved every moment of her time in London, but it was a joy to be in such beautiful, peaceful surroundings.

'I don't know how much you know about Knightsbrook, but this garden was designed for my great-great-grandfather in the mid-eighteenth century, by the famous landscape gardener Capability Brown,' the Duke said, playing the role of dutiful host.

Rosie nodded. When she had first arrived she had wondered whether the garden was a Capability Brown design, as it had the natural look the landscape gardener was famous for.

She gave a small cough. 'Capable who?'

'Capability Brown—he designed some of the most beautiful and highly regarded gardens in England.'

'Did he always plant so many trees? Trees are quite frightful, don't you think?'

He stopped, turned to face her, and frowned. 'You don't like *trees*?'

'No—awful things. They shed their leaves, making an unsightly mess all over the place. Not to mention all the terrible birds they attract. And as for the mess *those* frightful creatures make— well, the less said about that the better. I think the world would be much better off without so many trees.'

He looked along the path, then back towards the house. 'Then there's probably little point continuing our walk along this path, as it leads to a woodland area that contains some of the most established specimens of English trees to be found in the country.'

'Oh, no. I wouldn't want to see *that*.' Rosie gave a fake shudder. 'Has this estate got anything other than trees to look at?'

He stared at her for a moment, his brow furrowed. 'Perhaps you'd prefer to walk alongside the lake?'

She sighed, as if to say that if a lake was all he had to offer, then a lake it would have to be.

He led her to the gently curving serpentine lake that wound its way around the house. As they strolled slowly along its edge Rosie admired the centrepiece sculpture of Neptune, and the array of carved sea creatures that appeared to be frolicking in the waters. When the fountain sent water cascading high into the air, Rosie was tempted to clap her hands with delight at its playfulness.

'Is the lake more to your taste, Miss van Haven?

She forced her face to remain impassive. 'Lakes are all right, I suppose. But it's a shame it's got all those sculptures in it. Art is so distracting, don't you think?'

'You don't like art either?'

She shook her head vigorously and scowled. 'No—art is so *wasteful*, don't you think? All those galleries, and museums…theatres and whatnot. I'm sure they could all be put to much better use. Don't you agree?'

'Miss van Haven, you're…' He paused and looked around, as if struggling to find the right words.

Rosie smiled and waited for an appropriately disparaging comment that would seal her fate as a completely unacceptable future bride.

'You're quite unusual—aren't you, Miss van Haven?'

Quite unusual. It wasn't nearly as insulting as she would have liked, but it would have to do.

'Unusual? Me? No, I don't think so. I think it's the rest of the world that's unusual. All those people who like culture…plays, books, art, sculptures… They're the unusual ones.' She shuddered, as if the mere thought of art was abhorrent to her.

'In that case I suspect there will be little point showing you the family's collection of Old Masters.'

Rosie abruptly stopped walking and screwed up her face as if in pain. *No.* She had gone too far. Nothing would please her more than to see the FitzRoy art collection. One of the few things she knew about the family was that they had been collecting art for generations and had one of the finest collections outside the national art galleries. And now she had deprived herself of the opportunity to view some of the world's finest masterpieces.

She bit lightly on her tongue, to stop herself from crying out that she would give just about anything to see the collection. Anything, that was, except betray her promise to Arabella to make sure the Duke had no interest in marrying her.

'Yes, I suspect you're right—it would be a complete waste of time to show me *any* pictures,' she said through clenched teeth.

'Perhaps, then, we should sit awhile?'

He led her to a seat on the stone bridge that curved over the lake. While they looked out at the water and the woodland backdrop Rosie tried to think of a scheme that would convince Lord Ashton that, despite her claim to detest art, it would still be a good idea for him to show her the collection.

'Miss van Haven, there is something I must tell you. I hope you won't be offended, but it is essential that I tell you the truth.'

'I'm sure nothing you say will offend me, Your Grace.' After all, Rosie was the one who was trying her hardest to be offensive.

'You were invited here for the weekend under false pretences and I must let you know the true situation.'

She tilted her head. This was intriguing. 'False pretences?

'It was my mother's idea to invite you. I believe she has given you and your father the impression that I am interested in meeting you with the intention of looking towards a possible marriage. That is not the case. You're a very pretty young lady, Miss van Haven, and I'm sure you will one day make some man very happy, but I'm afraid that man won't be me.'

Had she heard him correctly? 'You don't want to marry me?'

'I'm sorry, Miss van Haven. As I said, I mean no offence. I don't wish to marry anyone. I don't know if you are aware that your father and my mother have put this scheme together without my approval, or even my knowledge. So, my apologies for the gross deception, but I don't want to marry you.'

Rosie clapped her hands and laughed with delight. 'That's wonderful news!'

With his eyebrows knitted together, he once again looked at her as if she were a curiosity. 'Wonderful? Am I to assume that you don't wish to marry either?'

She shook her head vigorously, still smiling and clapping. 'No, I most definitely do not. Why else do you think I put on that performance when I first arrived? Why else do you think I said that trees are horrid? Who thinks *trees* are horrid? No one! I was trying to make you dislike me so you wouldn't want to marry me.'

She had expected him to laugh as well, but he continued to frown. It seemed an inability to smile was another thing he had in common with those statues of Greek athletes.

'None of what you said was true?'

'Of course not.' She shook her head at his obvious statement.

'*Why* did you feel the need to put on such an act?'

'So you wouldn't want to marry me, of course.' Rosie was beginning to wonder if the handsome Duke was perhaps a bit dim-witted.

'You've been lying and pretending since the moment you arrived?'

Her smile faltered. 'Um… Well, yes, I guess I have. But I had to.'

The furrow in his brow deepened. 'Would it not have been easier to have told the truth—that you didn't wish to marry?'

'Well, perhaps, but it might have got complicated if you had been determined to marry *me*.'

'And play-acting *isn't* complicated? Lying *isn't* complicated?'

Rosie shrugged, unsure how to answer.

He looked out at the lake and sighed deeply. 'I've always found that lies inevitably cause complications, and often have far-reaching consequences for too many people. Telling lies might benefit the liar, but it almost always causes a great deal of problems for everyone else.'

Rosie wondered at his reaction, which seemed to be about something more than just her deceptive behaviour. His face looked so solemn, even melancholy, almost as if he was recalling some past hurt, some previous act of deception that had wounded him.

Her immediate impulse was to put her hand on his arm—to comfort him the way she often longed for someone to comfort her. She knew what it was like to have suffered in the past, to feel the need to hide your internal wounds from the world. But she did not know this man—would never really know him. So instead she did what she always did. She kept smiling.

He turned his attention back to her. 'Is anything you've said today been the truth?'

'Um…well, I'm definitely American.' She gave an embarrassed laugh.

'Anything else?'

Rosie looked out at the lake, bit the edge of her lip and struggled to find anything to say.

'In that case, shall we try and sort the truth from the lies?'

Rosie shook her head, then nodded, unsure whether telling the truth was a good idea or not.

'Let's start with trees. What do you think of trees?'

She laughed lightly with relief; that was something about which she was happy to tell the truth. 'I *love* trees. And I love the gardens designed by Capability Brown. I've seen many sketches of his work and I was hoping I'd get a chance to see some of his gardens while I was in England. I love the way he combines a natural look with little whimsical features—like the fountains and sculptures. It's quite stunning.'

The furrow in his forehead disappeared and he looked at her as if seeing her for the first time. 'And I take it you don't object to birds either?'

She laughed again. 'Who wouldn't love birds? Of course I love birds—*and* all other animals.'

'And art, sculptures, plays, books, paintings?'

'I'm not a complete philistine. I *love* art, sculptures, books, paintings, plays…all forms of culture.'

'In that case I suspect you *would* enjoy seeing the family's art collection?'

Rosie clapped her hands again. She had got her wish. 'Oh, yes. Yes, please. I'd love to.'

'Then I'd be delighted to show you. But I think there is one thing that I must do first.'

As he moved towards her along the bench Rosie's breath caught in her throat. What was he doing? What was happening?

'Your hat became dislodged when you spun your way down the entrance hall and is now sitting at a somewhat comical angle. Please allow me to set it right.'

Still holding her breath, she forced herself not to gasp when his fingers lightly brushed her temples as he attempted to remove her hatpin.

The whisper of his hands on her cheeks as he gently pulled the hat straight was as light as a feather, but the sensation was all-consuming. Fire erupted within her. Her cheeks burned and her heart pounded so loudly she was sure he must be able to hear its furious drumbeat.

He was so close she could feel the warmth of his body, could sense his physical strength, and she had to fight hard against the invisible force that was tempting her to move even closer towards him.

He gave the hat a final tug and leaned back to observe his handiwork. 'There—that's much better.'

Rosie released her breath and gasped in another, trying to relieve her light-headedness. Instead she breathed in the masculine scent of leather and musk and her heartbeat increased its ferocious tempo.

She swallowed several times and tried to breathe slowly, to regain the composure that his touch had so easily stripped away.

This would not do. This would not do at all. It didn't matter how handsome he was. It didn't matter what effect his touch had on her. The Duke was not for her. He didn't want to marry Arabella. And if he had no interest in Mr van Haven's daughter—a woman from New York's elite society, a woman with a substantial dowry and the prospect of an enormous inheritance—he certainly wouldn't be interested in Mr van Haven's impoverished ward.

It was foolish even to think such things, and any such illusions had to be put out of her head immediately. She was here for one purpose only: to save Arabella from an unwanted marriage. To be bedazzled just because the Duke had touched her would be madness. She had to stay focused on her task.

No, the Duke was certainly not for her. And

if she was to stop herself acting inappropriately in any unintended way she had to remember that at all times.

Alexander gazed down at the puzzling Miss van Haven. Her cheeks had once again turned a pretty shade of pink, and her bright blue eyes glistened as she gazed back at him.

Yes, puzzling was the only word he could use to describe her. From her unconventional arrival to her confession that she had no more desire to marry than he did, she presented one big puzzle.

It seemed that telling lies was part of her nature, and that was something he would never countenance. If he had learnt one lesson from Lydia Beaufort it had been about the destructive nature of lies. Lydia had once been a young woman of great promise, but lies had ruined her life and her downfall had all but destroyed him in the process. Miss van Haven's lies might be less destructive than Lydia's, but they were lies all the same.

And Arabella's reason for lying—that it was less complicated than telling the truth—was no excuse. It appeared that Miss van Haven could challenge his mother when it came to a lack of logical thinking.

But there was something about her that he found undeniably attractive. Something he couldn't define. He rubbed his fingers together and could almost feel the touch of her silky-smooth skin, like a soft, creamy magnolia blossom.

But it wasn't that. Nor was it her pretty face or her slim-waisted figure. It wasn't the way she laughed so readily, nor the way she smelled of delicate spring flowers after a rain shower. Nor was it the unfathomable depths of her blue eyes. But there was definitely *something* about her. Why else would he have felt compelled to straighten her hat, when merely informing her that it had become dislodged was all that had been required.

He realised he had been staring at her for longer than propriety would allow, so quickly looked away and out at the lake. What did it matter if she was a beautiful young woman? Lydia had also been pretty and sweet, with a charming laugh...

'So, Miss van Haven,' he said, as soon as he had resumed his usual sense of equanimity. 'We've established that you like nature and art. Am I now seeing the real Arabella van Haven?'

'Oh, yes!' She gave a light, tinkling laugh. 'What you see is what you get.'

'No more lies.'

She coughed slightly, and her cheeks turned a deeper shade of pink. 'No more lies.'

Her assertion did nothing to unravel the puzzle. She claimed to be telling the truth now, but her tightly held smile and rapidly blinking eyes appeared to make a mockery of that claim. She was still holding something back, but what that was Alexander had no idea.

Surely it was of no matter what Miss van Haven might or might not be holding back. She was not Lydia Beaufort. He was not going to marry her. Her lies could not hurt him.

And he had achieved his goal. He had informed her that they would not be marrying, and on that he and Miss van Haven were in complete agreement. That was all that mattered.

It was time to put all speculation about this unusual American heiress to one side. Now that their awkward conversation about marriage was behind them, he could relax and simply play the role of good host.

He stood up and once again offered her his arm. 'If the real Arabella van Haven is interested in seeing the art collection, then I would be delighted to show her.'

She clapped her hands in a genuine show of bubbly excitement. 'Oh, yes, please! I've heard you have a Rembrandt that is reputed to be his best work, and a Vermeer, and several Gainsboroughs that are said to be exquisite.'

She stood up and placed her hand on his arm.

'Then shall we?' he said. 'It will also get you away from these horrid trees.'

Alexander found himself unexpectedly pleased when she playfully patted his arm in response to his teasing.

He looked around for the trailing maid, but she was nowhere in sight. 'We seem to have lost our chaperon,' he said.

'Oh, yes, Nellie. She's probably found something more entertaining to do than watch us. I hope you don't mind?'

He shook his head. Surely it should be *she* who should mind, not him. Yes, she was quite a puzzling young lady...

They retraced their steps along the path. Then he led her through the house to the gallery that contained many of the family's major paintings—including the Rembrandt she had remarked upon.

When she saw the self-portrait she stopped. Her hand went to her neck and he heard a quick intake of breath.

'It's beautiful. It's literally breathtaking,' she whispered, transfixed by the painting.

Alexander nodded. He had seen the self-portrait countless times, but its beauty still affected him deeply. He was inexplicably pleased that it had the same effect on Miss van Haven.

They stood, side by side in silent admiration.

'His sensitivity is superb,' she murmured. 'He's painted himself smiling, but he's still managed to capture a sense of tragedy in his eyes,'

Alexander looked down at Miss van Haven, impressed by her insight. It was exactly what he had thought when he first saw her—that there was a sense of tragedy behind her smiling eyes.

Rembrandt had gone from poverty to wealth and back to poverty, and had suffered deeply as a result. Arabella van Haven had been born into privilege and lived the life of a wealthy daughter of a prominent New York banker. And yet she had the look of one who had quietly suffered. Alexander couldn't help but wonder why.

He led her to a painting on the other side of the gallery, to avoid any further contemplation of what had caused Miss van Haven's sad eyes. 'The Vermeer is slightly more cheerful, but no less powerful.'

She gazed as if enchanted at the portrait of a beautiful young woman playing a lute. 'It's wonderful. He's really captured how a woman looks when she's absorbed in her performance. It reminds me so much of a friend of mine who loves to act.'

'Who might that be?'

She shook her head. 'Just a friend in New York.' She looked up at him and smiled. 'She often looks like that when she's performing— completely lost in the part, as if the real Ara—as if she no longer exists.'

Alexander led her slowly around the gallery,

stopping at the paintings by Gainsborough and at the portraits of his ancestors painted by Sir Joshua Reynolds.

'I think if I lived here I would never leave this room. You're so lucky, Your Grace.' She looked up at him, her eyes sparkling with the pleasure and passion that great art clearly evoked in her.

'Alexander—please call me Alexander. Your Grace sounds so stuffy,' he said, surprising himself with his lack of formality.

She gave another musical laugh. 'In that case you must call me…' She hesitated. 'You must call me Arabella.'

'Arabella.' He savoured the name. 'You're right, Arabella, and it is a room in which I spend a great deal of time. Unfortunately many of these paintings are going to have to be sold to pay my father's debts. We will have to enjoy them while they're still here.'

Her eyes grew wide. 'Surely not? It would be terrible if they were lost to the family—especially the ones that are portraits of your ancestors.'

'Yes, it is unfortunate.' Alexander exhaled to try and drive out his annoyance.

Those paintings would indeed have to be sold to cover his father's debts. Paintings that had been in his family for generations would be sold off because of that man's lying, cheating and irresponsible behaviour.

'It's unfortunate, but I intend to sell them to public art galleries, so they can be enjoyed by as many people as possible.'

'Good.' She nodded her approval. 'The more people who can see these exquisite artworks and experience the kind of pleasure I have today the better.'

As she stared at the painting she chewed lightly on her lower lip and tipped her head to one side.

'But it would still be better if they could remain in the house—especially the portraits of your ancestors. It's a shame you can't open the house to the public. Then people could pay a small entrance fee and enjoy the gardens and the woodlands, the lake and the art. It would be a lovely day out.'

Alexander stared at her, taken aback by the unusual and progressive suggestion of opening the house to the public. 'Yes, it's a nice idea—but I can't see my mother tolerating anyone except invited guests in the house. Even when I invite engineers and other professional people Mother can barely tolerate their presence. And these are people who are going to help transform the estate and make it profitable—not people just having "a lovely day out".'

She wandered over to the portrait of his great-great-grandmother, painted by Sir Joshua Reynolds. 'Well, she tolerated me and my antics when

I first arrived. Perhaps she's more adaptable than you think. And it would mean all these wonderful paintings could stay in the house, where they belong.'

'I suspect Mother would tolerate anything from you if she thought there was a chance we might be married.'

The edges of her lips pulled down in mock concern. 'Oh, dear. She's not going to take kindly to hearing we have agreed that neither of us wants to marry.'

'Unfortunately, Miss van Haven…

She raised her finger in admonishment.

'Sorry—Arabella. Unfortunately, Arabella, my mother is not one to give up easily. You will have to prepare yourself for some concerted matchmaking from her this weekend. I urge you to be resolute.'

'Oh, I can be resolute, Alexander—believe me.' She smiled at him.

He did not doubt it. Arabella was obviously a woman who knew her own mind. She might have some unusual ways of getting what she wanted, but there was no denying she had admirable determination.

They continued their slow movement around the gallery, admiring each painting in turn, until they halted in front of a pastoral scene of two lovers embracing, their naked bodies entwined under the canopy of a sweeping oak tree.

Alexander had seen the painting many times, but never had it affected him so powerfully. With the memory of Arabella's silky skin still imprinted on his fingers he could all but feel the soft, yielding flesh of a woman's naked body against his own. He could imagine looking down into Arabella's eyes as she looked up at him with the same intensity as the woman in the portrait. Her lips would be parted, waiting for his kiss, her body responding to his caresses.

He coughed to chase away the inappropriate image that had invaded his thoughts. Then coughed again to clear his throat.

'It's stunning, isn't it?' he said, his voice strangled despite his repeated coughs. 'It's by an unknown artist. My great-grandfather bought it while he was on his grand tour of Europe as a gift for his future bride.'

'It's beautiful. She must have felt truly desired,' she murmured, her fingers lightly touching her own lips.

It seemed she too was deeply affected by the passion in the painting. He noted that her breath was coming in a series of rapid gasps, her face and neck were flushed, and she was gazing at the painting as if enraptured.

Alexander forced himself to lead her away

until they reached a much more suitable work to show a young lady—one that would have a less disturbing effect on his own equilibrium too.

But as he stared at an etching of Knightsbrook House made not long after it had been extended, with the west wing added in the early eighteenth century, all he could think of was the previous painting of those lovers entwined, of naked flesh, of parted lips waiting for a kiss…

He drew in a deep breath and exhaled loudly. This was ridiculous. He had no interest in Miss van Haven. No interest at all. He did not want to marry her. He did not want to marry anyone. And he most certainly did not want to marry an American heiress. He would *not* have the world thinking he married purely to restore the family's fortune. And if he did not have any interest in marrying her then, as a gentleman, he had no right to be thinking of her lying naked in his arms.

He coughed again. No, he could not—would not think of her in that way. She was a delightful young woman with whom he was having a pleasant time. That was all.

Perhaps it was simply that it had been such a long time since he had enjoyed the company of a young woman as much as he was enjoying himself now. Perhaps that was why his thoughts had gone off on tangents better reserved for the bawdy houses of London.

Whatever the reason, it would not do.

They moved on to the next painting, which was of the estate's garden, and he saw her smile at the small children depicted playing beside the lake. Seeing her delighted smile, he couldn't help but wonder why it was that such an attractive young woman was so set against marriage. He knew why *he* didn't wish to marry, but she must want marriage, children, a family of her own... For some reason it was a question he wanted answered.

'Arabella, when you said you didn't want to marry, you never told me the reason why.'

She looked up at him, her expression startled, then quickly turned back to look at the painting, her hands pulling at the lace on the cuffs of her sleeves. 'I...well. I... It's because...um... it's because I...um...' She blinked rapidly. Her gaze moved around the room, then settled on the painting of the two lovers. 'It's because I'm in love with another man—we're all but betrothed.'

As if punched in the stomach, Alexander winced. It was not the answer he'd expected but surely it was the most logical one. She was beautiful, sweet and funny. Of *course* she would have numerous men wanting to marry her. And for many men her father's fortune would only add to her appeal.

He drew in a series of quick breaths. What was *wrong* with him? The fact that she was in love with another man was of no matter. In fact it made things easier. There would be no difficulties in convincing his mother what a hopeless cause it was, trying to get them to marry.

He should be happy for Miss van Haven. And he *was* happy for her. Why wouldn't he be?

And, that aside, he had much more important things to think about than the romantic entanglements of an American heiress.

He turned from the painting. 'I believe it is time we joined the other guests.' He placed his hand gently on her back and led her towards the gallery door.

'Yes, I suppose you're right,' she mumbled, still blushing inexplicably, but nevertheless following his lead out through the door and into the corridor.

Why she should be blushing over her admission of being in love with another man he had no idea, but the reasons for Miss van Haven's blushes were of as little consequence to him as her romantic attachments.

He had done his duty as host. Now he had work to do. He had a devastated estate to rescue. It was that which demanded his full attention.

Only a fool would allow himself to get side-tracked by the frivolity of a visit by an American heiress, and one thing Alexander knew about himself: he was no fool.

Chapter Four

〜❦〜

Why had she said that? Of all the excuses she could have come up with why had she said she was in love with another man?

Usually she could think much faster than that when put on the spot. Instead she had said the first thing that had come into her head and invented a non-existent lover to explain why an American heiress would not be interested in marrying the eminently suitable Alexander FitzRoy, Lord Ashton, the handsome and charming Duke of Knightsbrook.

But she could hardly have told him the truth, could she? She couldn't tell him that the real Arabella van Haven didn't want to marry because her one and only true love was the theatre, and she was determined to dedicate herself to pursuing a career on the stage.

Nor could she tell him that she, Rosie Smith, had long ago resigned herself to remaining unmarried. As the ward of a wealthy man, she knew that none of the men who moved in Mr van Haven's circles would be interested in marrying a woman who had no money of her own and no dowry. How could she tell him that a man like him, who could trace his family back countless generations, was so far out of reach it would be a joke for her even to contemplate marriage to such a man.

And she certainly couldn't tell him that she wasn't Arabella van Haven. She had promised Arabella she would help her and her goal had been easily achieved. But she still couldn't reveal that secret without Arabella's knowledge. It would be a betrayal of her promise to her friend—something she would never do.

Instead she had lied to Alexander. Again.

She should have thought more clearly. She should have come up with a better reason—one that was closer to the truth than her invention of a beau for Arabella. Why had she done that? It must have been because that image of the two entwined lovers was still in her mind. That beautiful painting had made her realise that such passion would be something she would never experience. But it had still been a dim-witted thing to say, and Rosie could kick herself for her lack of clear thinking.

She would have to keep her head and her emotions in check for the rest of the weekend, so she didn't say or do anything so foolhardy again.

She took one last glance over her shoulder at the art works she would never see again as Alexander hurried her out of the gallery. Such a shame. She could have spent the rest of the day and the evening looking at the paintings, but it seemed Alexander had different ideas. It appeared he'd had enough of the gallery. Or he'd had enough of her company.

They rushed down the hall as if they were late for an important appointment, his hand on her back hurrying her forward. It was apparent that now Alexander had done as his mother had commanded—had shown her the gardens and done his duty to his guest—he wanted rid of her.

Rosie tried hard not to be offended. It hardly mattered, really. So he was suddenly tired of her company and wanted to end their time alone together? It mattered not one jot.

And yet previously he had been so attentive to her. Right up till the time she had told him she was in love with another man. But there could be no connection between them; that would be too ridiculous. He had no interest in her. He had said so himself. And yet…

Rosie dismissed such scatter-brained thoughts. Even if his change in demeanour had come about because she had told him about the man she supposedly loved, it was the man American heiress Arabella van Haven loved—a woman from a respectable wealthy family. Not poor orphaned Rosie Smith.

Whatever his reason for such haste, trying to figure it out was pointless speculation.

As they rushed down the corridors towards the drawing room Rosie told herself she would not be offended by his determination to be rid of her. After all, what did it matter? She had got what she'd come for. Arabella was safe from an unwanted marriage. She had seen a beautiful garden, and viewed some exquisite paintings that few people got to see. That was a memory she would treasure always. Her plan had worked—not in the way she had envisaged, but it had still worked. Surely that was a satisfying conclusion?

All she had to do now was relax and enjoy the rest of her weekend in this grand home.

She glanced up at Alexander. His handsome face was set like stone as he focused straight ahead. It was as if he had one purpose and one purpose only: to end his time with Rosie as quickly as possible.

They reached the drawing room and she almost expected him to push her in, slam the doors behind her and make his escape. Instead he stood politely behind her, waited for the footman to open the doors, then followed her in.

The stately room was filled with the murmur of polite conversation as the assembled guests took afternoon tea. Fires crackled in several fireplaces, struggling to warm the expansive room, which held a slight chill despite the mild spring afternoon.

Rosie quickly scanned the room and took in every aspect of its opulence—from the large crystal chandelier suspended from the soaring engraved ceiling down to the intricate silk carpets that adorned the polished oak flooring. More of the family's art collection was on display here. The walls were filled with paintings, and every surface seemed to be decorated with artefacts and antiques—presumably collected by Alexander's many wealthy ancestors.

Rosie could only hope she would have an opportunity during the weekend to admire them more closely.

The Dowager was engrossed in conversation with a group of elderly women. When she saw Rosie and Alexander she instantly excused herself, rose from the chaise longue and with a purposeful swish of her black satin skirt walked over to join them.

Her gaze quickly moved from Rosie to Alexander and back again, giving her every appearance of making an assessment as to just how close her plan of marrying off her son to a wealthy heiress was to completion.

'There you two young people are,' she said. 'You were away so long I thought perhaps you had eloped!'

Alexander's body stiffened beside Rosie. She looked up and could see his lips drawn into a tight grimace.

'No, Mother, you are quite wrong. Yet again.'

'Oh, well, never mind,' the Dowager continued, ignoring the note of censure in Alexander's voice. 'I'm pleased you have had a chance to get better acquainted. Did you enjoy your tour of the grounds, Miss van Haven? I hope Alexander showed you just how beautiful Knightsbrook is—particularly when the trees are in blossom. Although *I* think it's beautiful in every season of the year.'

Rosie smiled politely. Now that the issue of marriage had been settled between her and Alexander there was no need to try and shock the Dowager with her bad behaviour. She could be herself. Well, not quite herself. She still had to be Arabella. But she didn't have to pretend to be a completely unacceptable potential bride who posed a constant threat to priceless heirlooms.

'Oh, yes, he did—and you're right. It is beautiful. I'm sorry we took so long, Your Grace, but Alexander also showed me your family's magnificent collection of paintings in the gallery, and I'm afraid we lost all sense of time.'

The Dowager beamed a delighted smile. 'I see you two have become quite familiar and are on first-name terms already. I'm very happy to hear it.'

Alexander returned his mother's smile with a frown. 'I apologise, Mother, for keeping Miss van Haven from the other guests.' His expressionless voice was a stark contrast to his mother's enthusiasm.

'So, how much of the estate did you get the chance to see, Miss van Haven?' the Dowager asked, drawing Rosie's attention away from the frowning Alexander. 'No doubt Alexander told you we have more than five thousand acres of land and that our gardens are among the finest in England?'

Alexander sighed loudly. 'You're starting to sound like a salesman, Mother.'

'Don't be vulgar, Alexander.' The Dowager's smile faltered slightly, before returning, just as large as before, as she focused her attention back on Rosie. 'I hope he told you that the FitzRoys have lived on this land since the fifteenth century? The house is reputed to be one of the most elegant in the country, with more than two hundred rooms. Not that I've counted them, of course. That includes the summer and winter parlours and two formal dining rooms, as well as the break-fast room, three drawing rooms, the ballroom, and countless bedchambers to accommodate as many guests as you could possibly wish to enter-tain. Do you like to entertain, Miss van Haven?'

Rosie forced herself not to smile as she watched Alexander roll his eyes. Instead she nodded non-committally.

'And every part of this house is desperately in need of extensive and very expensive renovation work,' he said.

The Dowager's lips drew into a tight line and her nostrils flared. She sent Alexander a quick, narrow-eyed glare then resumed smiling at Rosie. 'And you say that Alexander showed you the gal-lery? Indeed, it contains many priceless works of art—but it houses only a fraction of the family's collection, which can be found in every room of the house.'

Alexander's frown deepened further. 'And many of those works of art will have to be sold to cover our mounting debts.'

'Oh, Alexander, you can be such a bore some-times,' the Dowager snapped.

Rosie looked from Alexander to the Dowager and back again. It was as if she were watching a tennis match, played by two equally determined and equally matched opponents.

The Dowager continued to frown at her son,

and then, as if remembering herself, she smiled at Rosie. 'Not that he's a bore, *really*. This is most unlike him. Usually he's not in the least bit serious. Oh, yes, Alexander *loves* to have fun and live life to the full.'

Rosie bit the edge of her top lip to stifle a giggle. The supposedly fun-loving Alexander his mother was describing was as far from the serious, disapproving man standing beside her as it was possible to get.

'Really, Your Grace?' Rosie tried hard not to laugh. 'In that case I look forward to seeing Alexander perform a few party tricks.'

The Dowager flicked a nervous look in Alexander's direction, her smile twitching at the edges. Alexander glared back at her, as if challenging his mother to try and talk her way out of her outrageous claim.

Instead of attempting the impossible, she took Rosie's arm. 'There will be plenty of time for that later, but now our other guests are anxious to meet you.'

They swept their way around the large room and Rosie was introduced to Lord This and Lady That, the Countess of This and the Earl of That. If the assembled guests were anything to go by it seemed the FitzRoys really did mix in exclusive society. There was not a Mr or Mrs among them, with everyone in the room bearing a title from Duke down to Baron.

And each guest, no matter what their title, reacted in exactly the same manner when they were introduced to Rosie—with enthusiastic delight, as if they really were meeting the future Duchess of Knightsbrook. She was greeted with smiles, nods of approval, and even the occasional curtsey from the assembled aristocrats.

It seemed the Dowager was so convinced she was going to marry Alexander that she had all but announced the engagement already.

Alexander was right. The Dowager was a very determined woman. But unfortunately for her she was going to discover that both Rosie and Alexander were equally resolute that they would not be wed.

Their circuit of the large room took them to the last guest, a rather severe elderly woman standing by the fire. The Dowager seemed to hesitate, her smile quivering slightly, before she smiled and made the introductions.

'Lady Beaufort, may I introduce Arabella van Haven? She is our guest from America.'

Lady Beaufort's straight posture grew more rigid and her nose rose higher in the air as she tilted back her head and raked her gaze over Rosie from head to toe, then back again. 'So you're the banker's daughter?'

Rosie's fists clenched at her sides. Since her father had lost all his money through no fault of his own, reducing their family to a state of poverty, Rosie had been forced to endure being snubbed, insulted and belittled by people who had once treated her family with respect.

Through bitter experience she had learnt to let such behaviour wash over her. So she did what she always did in such circumstances: breathed in deeply, forced herself to relax her tensely gripped hands and smiled her sunniest smile.

'That's right. I'm the banker's daughter—Arabella van Haven. How do you do?'

She received the expected glare in return, which only caused Rosie to smile more brightly.

'I hear you're seeking a titled husband?' Lady Beaufort said after a prolonged silence.

Several guests nearby gasped at this blatant breach of the rules of polite conversation, but their shock didn't stop them from leaning forward, eager to hear more of this exchange.

'Oh, come, come, Lady Beaufort,' the Dowager said with a false laugh. 'Miss van Haven is here to enjoy our hospitality. If she and Alexander should happen to fall in love, well…'

'I'm just pleased my dear daughter Lydia is not here to see this shameless behaviour.'

The Dowager's mouth opened and closed as she gasped for something to say.

'And now that I've met the banker's daughter who is trying to buy herself a title I think I'll take my leave.'

Lady Beaufort swept past Rosie, causing her to jump out of her way to avoid getting trampled in her bull-like progress.

But Rosie had failed to notice one of the couples who had moved closer to hear the conversation. She stepped back on to the listening man's foot, causing him to cry out and send his teacup clattering to the ground.

The sound of shattering china brought all conversation to a sudden halt as every head turned in their direction.

'Oh, look what the clumsy little thing has done!' Lady Beaufort said as a young maid scrambled on the floor to retrieve the pieces of broken porcelain. 'It's a shame these Americans don't know how to act in polite society.'

'Lady Beaufort, I think you should leave. Now.'

Rosie heard Alexander's commanding voice behind her.

'Oh, don't worry. I'm leaving. I'm quite particular about the company I keep. Thank goodness Lydia was saved from seeing this appalling display.'

She gave Rosie another disapproving look and swept out of the room, her exit watched by every one of the assembled guests.

'I think our guests are in need of a drink somewhat stronger than tea,' Alexander announced, and signalled to the servants, who began pouring glasses of port.

Conversation instantly erupted in the room, but it was no longer the murmur of polite chatter. The assembled guests were talking loudly, all at once, and judging from the repeated glances in Rosie's direction they were all speculating on what had just happened.

Alexander leaned down and whispered in her ear. 'Would you like to take some air, Arabella?'

She nodded rapidly. She most certainly did want to escape. The last thing she felt like doing was remaining in the drawing room while a group of gossiping lords and ladies discussed that bizarre outburst.

Rosie had been snubbed by some of New York's finest snobs, and she had smiled through every subtle and not so subtle insult. But she was decidedly shaken by Lady Beaufort's outburst.

Why this woman should hate her was unfathomable. Surely being a banker's daughter was not so shameful? Particularly when that banker was one of America's wealthiest men and therefore, by extension, one of the world's wealthiest men. And why was Lady Beaufort so concerned about her daughter not being exposed to someone like

Arabella? And why should she care whether she married Alexander?

This was clearly more than just good old-fashioned snobbery.

Chapter Five

Alexander led Arabella out through the drawing room towards the French doors. Voices fell silent as they passed, and each guest turned and attentively followed their progress as they walked across the room. He'd leave his guests to their gossip and speculation, and he was sure there would be an excessive amount of that. All that was important was to get Arabella away from the wagging tongues.

As he closed the doors behind them every gleeful face turned in their direction, all eyes peering out of the large sash windows with insatiable curiosity.

He exhaled with impatience. No doubt talking about that incident would keep them entertained for many weeks to come. It was a pity they did not have more to occupy their time, but with wealth and a multitude of servants came plenty of free hours to gossip.

For once Alexander was grateful that he had such an enormous task ahead of him in saving the estate.

They walked down some stone stairs and across a gravel pathway to a wooden bench in front of the garden.

Arabella seated herself, then looked back over her shoulder at the house. 'Well, that was certainly strange.'

'Strange' was an understatement. Alexander gazed at her, amazed at her composure. But her lack of distress was neither here nor there. She should not have been exposed to Lady Beaufort's wrath.

Alexander had difficulty understanding why his mother had invited her to an event such as this. It was inevitable that Lady Beaufort would be offended by the possibility of Alexander being betrothed to another woman when he had once been betrothed to Lady Beaufort's daughter.

He could only assume his mother had invited her because Lady Beaufort remained a doyen of society, despite Lydia's fall from grace, and it would be thought a folly to slight her. But whatever his illogical mother had been thinking she had caused upset to Arabella, and that was unacceptable.

The American heiress had done nothing to deserve such treatment. She had been set up for a marriage she didn't want by her father and his mother, and invited into this house under false pretences. And now she had been insulted by one of the guests.

Alexander was unsure why he felt such a strong need to protect her—whether it was just a natural instinct or something stronger. Whatever it was, he did not want her subjected to such outrages again.

'I'm sorry. I hope you are not too distressed by Lady Beaufort's rudeness. Unfortunately she has suffered some major disappointments in her life, and that has turned her into a rather unpleasant woman. But she had no right to take it out on you.'

Arabella shook her head. 'That's usually the way, isn't it? When people are unhappy they tend to lash out. And, no, of course I'm not upset.' She looked over her shoulder at the house. 'I'm a bit confused, but not upset.'

Alexander shook his head, dragged in a long, unsteady breath and tried not to think of what had caused that outburst. He did not want to think of how he had been betrayed by Lydia Beaufort, or of how she had caused him so much pain that he had sworn that he would never allow himself to be hurt like that again.

'Lady Beaufort's daughter Lydia was a lovely young woman and we were betrothed to be married.'

Arabella's eyes grew wide. He obviously had her full attention.

'But you are not any more?' she asked, her voice barely audible.

'No, not any more. Lydia…' He dragged in a deep breath. 'Lydia changed. She did things that caused her to be shunned from society.'

He paused again. Arabella did not need to know the full extent of why Lydia had suffered such a fate. Nor did she need to know how she had almost destroyed him in the process. She merely needed an explanation for Lady Beaufort's outburst.

'Her family is one of the best-connected in England, but even that couldn't save her when she chose to live a life that has shocked many people,' he said, hoping that would suffice.

'And Lady Beaufort blames *you* for this?'

He exhaled a ragged breath and nodded. 'Yes—but she has no right to blame you.'

'I'm sorry, Alexander. Is this something you'd rather not talk about?'

He shook his head. 'It is of no matter,' he said, with as much nonchalance as he could muster. 'I'm used to being on the receiving end of Lady Beaufort's misdirected rage. But you should never have been subjected to it, and I am truly sorry. If I had known she would behave like that towards you I would have insisted my mother not invite her.'

Arabella shrugged. 'You've got nothing to apologise for. And I can't really criticise anyone's bad behaviour—not after my somewhat unconventional arrival. At least your mother was standing right next to me. She could see that it wasn't my fault that the teacup was shattered. I wouldn't want her to think breaking porcelain is my special party trick.' She gave a little laugh and patted him on the arm. 'Let's just forget about that horrible Lady Beaufort and pretend it never happened.'

Alexander could hardly believe it. He should be comforting *her*; instead she was patting his arm in a reassuring manner and making light of the incident. She really was quite remarkable. An experience like that would have had most woman reaching for the smelling salts, but she was completely calm. He wondered what had given this young woman such resilience—something usually lacking in the gently reared women of his class.

'You will not have to worry about her being rude to you again. After that outburst I will make it clear to her that she is not welcome in this house.'

'Oh, you don't have to do that. A few insults aren't going to ruffle me. I'm made of stronger stuff than that and I have learnt to cope with much worse.'

Alexander looked into her deep blue eyes, curious to know why a woman who had lived the pampered and protected life of an heiress would need to be strong. 'And why is that? Why do you need to be strong, Arabella?'

Once again he saw that sadness come into her eyes, before she shrugged her shoulders and smiled at him. 'Perhaps it just comes naturally to someone whose grandfather was a mule driver,' she said, in her now familiar flippant tone.

It seemed he was not going to get a serious answer to his question. He was not going to find out why that small shadow of sadness seemed to cloud her otherwise sunny disposition.

'Perhaps you are right. Although I suspect there is more to you than you like to reveal to the world.'

Her cheeks burned a brighter shade of red, and she blinked repeatedly before giving a dismissive laugh. 'No, there's nothing more to reveal. I'm just your average young lady with no hidden depths.'

Her words contradicted her look of discomfort. It was obvious to Alexander that Arabella was anything but average. It was also obvious that she was not going to reveal anything to him.

And he ought to leave her with her secrets. After all, what business was it of his?

'Well, no doubt that inner strength is going to be called upon soon, when we have to face the guests again. I'm afraid that after Lady Beaufort's outburst you will undoubtedly be the main topic of conversation for quite some time. You will need to prepare yourself for some curious looks at the very least, and no doubt some very impertinent questioning.'

'Oh, that doesn't worry me.' She looked over her shoulder, back at the house. 'It won't be long before someone else makes an inexcusable faux pas—such as using the wrong knife for the fish course—and then they'll be so scandalised that they'll move on from discussing me to some other unfortunate victim.'

It seemed Arabella had the same low opinion of the ridiculous foibles of the gentry as he did himself.

Growing up, he had spent as much time as he could away from this house. His father's riotous gambling parties had often gone on for weeks at a time, and he and Charlotte had taken refuge in the welcoming cottage of Annie, the wife of a tenant farmer, who worked in dairy. It was during his time with Annie and her husband that he had learnt how hard the tenants worked, tilling the soil and making the money which his father and his friends squandered. In contrast to Annie's warm and welcoming ways, the excesses, rituals and snobbery of his own class had seemed absurd, but it was unusual to meet someone who thought the same way as him.

'You must cause quite a stir amongst New York society with that attitude,' he said.

She shrugged her shoulders and shook her head slightly. 'Well, perhaps—but it's an attitude I tend to keep to myself and only share with my closest friends.'

'Your closest friends? Does that include this man you are in love with? Does he share your irreverent attitude to society?'

Damn. He had vowed to ask her nothing about the man, but the questions had come out before Alexander had realised he was asking. Questions that seemed now to hang in the air between them.

Hadn't he told himself he did not want or need to know anything about the man? And yet at the same time he wanted to know everything there was to know about this man Arabella loved. He wanted to know what she felt for him and how he made her feel. And did this man know the reason for the sadness that cast a shroud over her bright blue eyes?

But why should it matter? She was a woman who was in love with another man, and he was unlikely to see her again after this weekend.

And yet it did matter.

His body tensed as he waited for the answers he both did and did not want to hear.

Chapter Six

Rosie squirmed uncomfortably on the wooden bench. How was she supposed to answer such a question? *Did* she share such thoughts with her non-existent lover? *Would* she share such things with him? Probably. Wasn't that what people in love did? But how was Rosie supposed to know? She had never been in love. Never expected to be in love.

She glanced in Alexander's direction. Yes, she could imagine that a woman who was in love would want to tell her man about herself, about her thoughts, her feelings. They would surely want to share their troubles and offer each other comfort and support. A woman in love with a man would also want to hear *his* thoughts, *his* feelings, and to know everything there was to know about him.

If a woman was in love with a man like Alexander she was sure that was how she would be feeling.

She turned to look straight ahead. But she had never been in love—not with this imaginary man, and certainly not with Alexander.

Rosie started. Where had *that* thought come from? Of course she wasn't in love with Alexander. The mere idea of it was ludicrous.

She gave a little laugh, and took another quick sideways look in Alexander's direction. He was staring at her, waiting for her to answer. An uncomfortable silence stretched out between them. Her cheeks burned hotter. She had to say something. *Anything.*

'Oh, you know…we talk of this and that. And I suppose he's a bit like me when it comes to not taking things too seriously.'

Would that be enough to satisfy his curiosity?

He looked down at her, then stared out at the garden and clasped his hands tightly together. 'What sort of man is he, this man you are in love with?'

Rosie winced. It seemed Alexander wasn't satisfied with her vague answer, and wasn't going to let the subject drop. She cast another quick look in his direction and wondered why he was so curious about her imaginary beloved. He had reacted so strangely when she had first told him, and now seemed to want to know all about him.

But it didn't matter what *he* was thinking. She needed to concentrate. Needed to answer his question. So, what sort of man would he be, this fictional lover of hers? Rosie had no idea, but she had to say something.

'Oh, you know. He's just a man.'

Alexander turned and looked down at her, his eyebrows knitted together. '"Just a man"? He's the man you say you are in love with—the man you're all but betrothed to—and you dismiss him as "just a man"?'

Why was he interrogating her like this? Was he trying to make her feel uncomfortable? If that was his intention then he was succeeding. But it seemed he was uncomfortable too. He was staring down at her, his jaw tense, his hands tightly clasped together as he waited for her answer.

Could he be jealous?

Rosie shook her head slightly. No, she was being ridiculous. He was curious, that was all, and she should be thinking of an answer to his question—not letting her mind drift off to wistful fantasies.

She shrugged as she struggled to find one. What could she say? Especially as the man wasn't even that. He wasn't *just a man*—he wasn't a man at all. He was a figment of her imagination.

'He must at the very least have a name?'

'Of course he's got a name.' Rosie gave a light, dismissive laugh.

He raised his eyebrows.

A name...a name. What on earth would her beloved be called?

She quickly scanned the garden, looking for inspiration. She focused on a statue of Pan, playing his pipes. Pan? Was that a good name? No. Pan might be suitable for a Greek god, but not for a young man in love with the daughter of an influential New York banker.

She spied a ginger cat, curled up and sleeping at Pan's feet.

'Tom—his name is Tom. Thomas, actually, although I call him Tom...sometimes Tommy.' She all but shouted her answer.

'And does Tom, Thomas, sometimes Tommy, have a surname?'

A surname? Yes, he probably would have a surname. But what could it be?

Her gaze shot to the other sculptures. She was desperate for inspiration. Hercules? No. Neptune? No.

She looked at the garden instead, at the sea of daffodils stretched out in front of them, their yellow heads bobbing in the slight breeze. Tom Daffodil? No. She took in the sculpted topiary. Then her frantic gaze shot to the rose garden, laden with multi-coloured buds, ready to burst forth. She looked up to the line of rustling oak trees.

Still no name occurred to her.

An elderly man pushing a squeaking wheelbarrow packed high with weeds and dead branches appeared from behind the line of oak trees and began walking up the path, his boots crunching on the gravel.

'Gardener. His name is Thomas Gardener.'

She slumped back on to the bench in relief. Thank goodness for that. Now he had a name the subject could be dropped and hopefully never mentioned again.

'Thomas Gardener…' Alexander said slowly, as if considering the name. 'And I take it your father does not approve of this Thomas Gardener? Or he would not have sent you across the ocean in pursuit of a husband. What exactly is wrong with him? Why doesn't your father wish you to marry him?'

Rosie sat up straight. Why, indeed? Why would Mr van Haven not want a woman who was not his daughter to marry a non-existent man who was named after a sleeping cat and an elderly man with a wheelbarrow? It was a difficult question to answer.

'Um…he doesn't approve of him because…' Once again she looked around the garden for inspiration. 'Because…' The garden refused to reveal a suitable reason.

She turned to the house and quickly scanned up and down its four-storey exterior. She spotted the balconies on the second floor, and the last play she had seen before sailing for England jumped to mind.

'Because he's the son of my father's sworn enemy, who is the head of a rival New York banking family.'

It was a bit melodramatic, but it would have to do. Normally Rosie prided herself on being able to think under pressure, but the pressure she was feeling now was far greater than any she had felt before. It was as if all Alexander had to do was raise a questioning eyebrow and she lost all ability to think clearly.

'Oh, so you're like Romeo and Juliet? A couple of young star-crossed lovers whose fathers will never countenance the marriage?' His words dripped with derision.

Rosie pulled at her collar, which seemed to be getting tighter and tighter as she dug herself deeper and deeper into a pit of lies.

She stared straight ahead, hoping his disparaging comment hadn't been made because he had seen her staring at the balcony and made the connection with Shakespeare's famous romantic tragedy.

'Well, not really.' She gave a light laugh, which she hoped didn't sound as false to Alexander as it did to her. 'It's not quite so romantic. After all, they're boring bankers and we're not living in Verona.'

'And is it because of your father's disapproval of this Thomas Gardener's family that he sent you to England? Is that why he's trying to marry you off to someone else?'

'That…and because he wants his daughter to have a title; he wants her to be a duchess.'

Rosie smiled. Didn't it feel good to finally be saying something that was true? Well, almost true. Mr van Haven didn't care a fig whether Rosie married or not, but he most certainly wanted *Arabella* married, and married to a man with a title—the higher up the social strata the better. A daughter with a title would place him well above the rest of the New York elite—not just in money, but also in social status.

'So it seems your father is going to be disappointed?'

'Mmm, I suppose he will be…'

In more ways than one—especially when he finds out that Arabella has not only refused to give up her aspirations of becoming an actress, but has arrived in England with the intention of pursuing a career on the London stage.

But that was a problem they would deal with at a later date.

'What about you, Alexander? Why don't *you* want to marry?'

Rosie tried to keep her question flippant. After all, she had merely asked the question to save her from telling more lies. Hadn't she?

If Alexander wanted to marry someone else that would mean Arabella was most definitely safe from an unwanted marriage. But the thought of Alexander in love with another woman, wanting to marry another woman, was doing strange things to her nervous system. Her stomach had clenched itself into a tight knot. Her breath was caught in her throat. And an odd light-headedness was making her dizzy.

It was so *wrong* for her to be feeling like this. What was causing her such pain? Could it be jealousy? Ridiculous. How could she feel jealous over a man she couldn't have? Or be jealous of a woman he might or might not be in love with, who might or might not exist?

No, it couldn't be jealousy. That was too ridiculous. But whatever it was she had to stop feeling like this. She had to stop it *now*.

'I have more important things to occupy my time. I have an estate to save,' he finally answered, his words brusque.

Rosie tilted her head slightly and cast him a

sideways glance. His answer was curious. He claimed to abhor lying and yet his words had been so terse. That, along with his clenched jaw and pressed lips, suggested he was not telling the entire truth.

Rosie knew she should just leave it there. What did it matter why he didn't want to marry? The fact that he didn't want to marry Arabella should be enough. But, like an open wound she couldn't stop prodding, she felt incapable of leaving the subject alone.

'Can't you save the estate and be married at the same time? They're not mutually exclusive activities.'

'My father has left substantial debts,' he said, his brow furrowed, his jaw tightly held. 'I would rather wait until I've cleared all those debts and the estate is once again capable of supporting the family. Then I would have something to offer a wife.'

Rosie was tempted to tell him he already had a lot to offer any woman. He was handsome, charming, kind and loyal. In every aspect he was the perfect man, and it was unlikely that she was the only woman to realise that.

'Surely that wouldn't matter if you met the right woman?' she said quietly.

Alexander made no response and Rosie mentally chastised herself. She had to stop asking these questions—especially as every question and every answer was causing that knot in her stomach to tighten another notch.

She took in a few deep breaths to try and loosen its grip and reminded herself that it didn't matter whether Alexander met any woman, the right one or not. It was none of her concern whether he wanted to marry, as long as he didn't want to marry Arabella. If he wanted to wait until he had saved the estate and restored the family's fortune then all the better. That meant it would be a long time before he considered taking a wife, and by then she and Arabella would be gone.

'Not all women think like that, Arabella—and certainly not aristocratic women,' he said finally. 'They and their families want a marriage that not only improves their position in society but also guarantees they will continue to live in the manner to which they are accustomed. My title is attractive on its own merits, but I am a long way from being able to guarantee the second. And I won't consider marriage until I can provide sufficiently for my wife.'

Rosie looked out at the expansive gardens and parklands, then back at the sweeping four-storey house behind her, with, as the Dowager had claimed, at least two hundred rooms, many of which contained priceless art works and treasures.

'And this wouldn't be enough?' she murmured in disbelief.

'No—a bankrupt estate with ever-mounting debts would *not* be enough. A backward estate that has not been managed properly for generations would not be enough. It needs to change. It needs to be modernised. Perhaps when that has been achieved I'll have the luxury of thinking about such things as marriage.'

'The right woman wouldn't care about any of that,' she said quietly. 'The right woman would want to work *with* you to make the estate viable. She would want to make your load lighter, not expect you to do all the work on your own and then hand it to her on a silver platter.'

He looked down at her and gazed deep into her eyes, as if trying to read her thoughts. 'Not all women are like you, Arabella,' he murmured.

Rosie swallowed away her embarrassment. No, not all women *were* like her. They didn't all lie. They didn't all pretend to be someone else. They didn't all tell tall tales about imaginary men and fake betrothals. And surely most women would be sensible enough to stop talking about something that made them feel so intensely uncomfortable? But then, as he'd said, Rosie was not like most women.

'You deserve to meet the right woman, Alexander. A woman who wants to marry *you*—not your title or your money, but *you*.'

There was so much more to Alexander than his title and his estate, and surely Rosie would not be the only woman to see this?

He gave a small, humourless laugh.

'You should marry a woman who wants to work with you to achieve your dreams,' she went on.

If Rosie had been in love with Alexander, and if he had been in love with her, that was what she would want. Not that there was any possibility of either of those laughable things ever happening.

He continued to gaze down at her, his deep brown eyes burning into hers. 'Thomas Gardener is a lucky man to have a fiancée who believes in supporting her future husband the way you do.'

His words were kind, but his captivating eyes contained an intensity that caused heat to burn through her body.

She swallowed, looked away, and fought to compose herself. *And the woman who eventually becomes the Duchess of Knightsbrook is even luckier*, she wanted to say, but knew she never would.

They sat in silence for a few moments, seemingly both absorbed in their own thoughts.

Rosie wondered what was going through Alexander's mind. Surely his thoughts couldn't be as confused as hers? *Nobody's* thoughts could be as confused hers.

It wasn't supposed to be like this. The plan had been so simple. But then, when she had come up with this plan over tea at the Ritz, she hadn't expected the Duke to be anything like Alexander. She hadn't expected him to be handsome. Nor had she expected him to be a proud, honest man who was determined to solve his financial problems without resorting to marrying for money.

And she hadn't expected him to make her feel things she should not be feeling—emotions she could hardly understand, even less put names to.

If only he had been a stuffy duke, set on marrying Arabella for her money, then she would have been in her element. She would have had enormous fun at his expense. Instead she was unsure what she was supposed to do, how she was supposed to behave, how she was even supposed to feel.

All she knew was that she shouldn't be feeling the way she was now.

The discreet cough of a footman broke the silence. 'Her Grace wishes to make you aware that it is time you dressed for dinner,' he said, and bowed then left.

'It looks as if we are going to have to face the gossips,' Alexander said, standing and taking Rosie's hand. 'As uncomfortable as this might be, as you are the guest of honour I fear it would be cause more of a stir for you not to appear at tonight's dinner. But of course if you'd rather not then I will tell my mother that you are indisposed.'

Rosie rose from the bench. She doubted his guests could make her feel any more uncomfortable than she did right now. 'No, it's of no mind. They can gossip about me as much as they like. I'm happy to be their source of entertainment.'

They retraced their steps up the path to the stairs.

'At least you won't have to worry about my mother matchmaking. You'll be saved that annoyance. When I tell her about Thomas Gardener even she will have to back down.'

Rosie halted. 'No, please don't do that,' she blurted out, gripping his arm with both hands. She could not have anyone else knowing about Arabella's non-existent beloved. If news of it got back to Mr van Haven it would cause huge problems for Arabella, and Rosie would never allow that to happen.

He raised a questioning eyebrow.

'If it got back to my father...' Rosie said desperately.

Alexander gently patted her hand. 'I understand, Arabella. If you want to keep your Mr Gardener a secret, it will not be revealed by me.'

A mixture of relief and shame swept over Rosie. Relief that she would not be causing any problems for Arabella, and shame that once again she had lied to an honourable man who deserved better.

But what else could she do? It seemed she was trapped inside a complicated story of her own invention—a story she seemed to make more complex every time she spoke.

'Thank you,' she mumbled, releasing her grip on his arm, and hoping she had told her last lie to Alexander.

Chapter Seven

'So, what's the gossip below-stairs?' Rosie sat on the embroidered stool in front of the mirror and looked up at Nellie's reflection.

It was a relief to be in the company of someone who knew who she really was. She could relax, because she didn't have to be constantly on her guard in case she said or did anything that would give her away.

She waited in expectation. Rosie knew that the best way to find out about anything that was happening was through the servants. Their outward appearance remained impassive as they went about their duties, but they saw and heard everything.

Nellie picked up a brush and ran long strokes through Rosie's hair in preparation for curling, braiding and threading it with ribbons, so it would look stylish for tonight's dinner.

More a friend than a servant, Nellie had been

with the van Haven family since she'd emigrated to America from Ireland when she was fourteen years old and had been hired as a scullery maid. Intelligent and talented, she'd quickly risen through the ranks to become a lady's maid.

Arabella was very much aware of just how lucky she was to have Nellie, and her abilities as a hairstylist had seen many of the New York society ladies try to lure her away—but to no avail. And Rosie knew that Nellie harboured ambitions that didn't involve spending the rest of her life as a servant.

'Well, the servants are all atwitter about you, so they are.' Nellie frowned as she teased out a knot in Rosie's hair. 'They're all in agreement that you'll make an excellent duchess. Even the ones who thought it wasn't appropriate to have an American have come around.'

'Except I'm Rosie. Remember? And the real Arabella doesn't want to be a duchess. That's why I'm here.'

Nellie shrugged, divided Rosie's hair into several sections and began rolling one of the long tresses. 'Of course I remember. I'm just repeating what the servants said. And they're all in agreement that they're looking forward to having you as their new mistress.'

'Well, it's good that it's not up to the servants to decide who the Duke is to marry, or they'd have me up the aisle in no time at all. Fortunately the Duke himself isn't the slightest bit interested in marrying me.'

Nellie stopped what she was doing and stared at Rosie's reflection. 'That's not what I heard.'

'Why? What did you hear?' Rosie turned on the stool to face Nellie, who frowned, placed her hands firmly on Rosie's shoulders and turned her back towards the mirror.

She picked up the fallen tress of hair and resumed rolling. 'They all think the Duke is completely smitten with you.'

'They *what*?' Rosie started to turn again, then saw Nellie's frown and remained facing forward. 'They think *what*? No, they're wrong. He's not interested in me in any way whatsoever.'

'Well, all the servants who were in the drawing room when you were being introduced to the other guests said he couldn't take his eyes off you. That he was watching you the whole time. And when that horrible Lady Beaufort had her outburst he was at your side immediately, being all protective, like.'

'He was?' Rosie tilted her head, only to have it straightened by Nellie. 'Well, I'm sure it means nothing. He was just being a gentleman.'

'Hmm…' Nellie said, her mouth full of hairpins and her hands occupied with threading silver ribbon through Rosie's hair. She stood back and admired her handiwork. 'And the footman said he hadn't seen His Grace so taken with a young lady since Lydia Beaufort.'

Rosie's gaze shot up to Nellie's reflection. 'What did they say about Lydia Beaufort?

Nellie frowned and put to rights a silver ribbon that Rosie's sudden movement had dislodged. 'I don't know. All I know is when her name was mentioned all the servants looked very serious—as if the footman had mentioned a forbidden topic. But Jennie, the parlour maid, said she thought you were prettier than Lydia anyway, and much nicer. Before she was shushed by the housekeeper.'

'Oh, she did, did she? She said I was prettier?' Rosie patted the side of her hair and tilted her head slightly to admire her reflection. 'Well, that's something, I suppose. So was there any other gossip?'

'No, but Jennie said that she thought you were smitten too. In fact, she said she'd never seen anyone look so dewy-eyed.'

Rosie looked up at Nellie's laughing reflection, then back at her own blushing face. 'Dewy-eyed? Me? Nonsense.'

'Hmm…'

'There's no "hmm" about it. Stop staring at me like that and help me into my dress.'

Flustered, Rosie rushed over to the wardrobe,

removed the gown from the hanger and began pulling it over her head.

'Stop doing that. You'll ruin your hair. And I think you're going to be needing this first.'

Rosie turned and saw Nellie holding up her corset. She exhaled loudly, handed the dress to Nellie and waited while she wrapped the corset around her waist, tied the laces tight and helped her into her bustle.

'Um…there's something I probably should tell you…' Rosie said, her cheeks still burning.

Nellie stopped brushing down the cambric fabric of Rosie's petticoat and waited.

'The Duke believes we're not going to be married because Arabella is in love with another man.'

Nellie's eyes grew wide. 'She *what*? When did this happen? Arabella never told me she was in love.'

'She's not really, but I had to make something up to explain why Arabella wouldn't be marrying the Duke. So I said that I am—or she is, really—in love with a man called Thomas Gardener, who is the son of Mr van Haven's arch enemy from a rival banking family.'

'Oh, Rosie, no—you didn't!' Nellie released a frustrated sigh. 'You always complicate things. You come up with a plan which seems to be simple and then you go and make it complicated. It was just the same when you and Arabella snuck off to the fair dressed as boys, so you could get work on the sideshows. You almost got away with it until you told the sideshow owner you had just returned from the sea, danced that silly jig and your hat fell off—revealing your hair. He nearly hog-tied the pair of you. And then there was that time you tried to trick your tutor by...'

Rosie held up her hands to stop the criticism. 'This is nothing like that. I was put on the spot. I had to come up with *something*.'

'Couldn't you just have said that you want to remain single and have no interest in marrying anyone? Why did you have to invent this Thomas Gardener? And why make him Mr van Haven's arch enemy? Did you *have* to get so overly dramatic?'

Rosie shrugged. 'I was flustered. But what's done is done. Anyway, it's supposed to be a secret. I've asked Alexander not to tell anyone. I just thought I'd tell you in case one of the servants finds out. I didn't want you to be taken by surprise.'

'Hmm...' Nellie frowned in disapproval as she lowered the dress carefully over Rosie's head and began doing up a row of buttons at the back.

'So, what else did the servants say about Lady Beaufort's outburst?' Rosie asked, changing the subject away from her blunder.

'Well, not much. Jennie was annoyed that she had to scramble around her feet to retrieve all those tiny pieces of shattered porcelain, and the housekeeper was worried about the damage the tea had done to the rug, but that was about it.'

Rosie shook her head in disbelief. 'What? No one thought it was odd? No one had any comments or opinions?'

'Apparently she's been a bit odd since Lydia got into some sort of trouble. The servants all wonder why the Dowager continues to invite her, but she's fabulously wealthy, so I suppose everything else gets forgiven.'

'What sort of trouble did Lydia get into?'

Nellie shrugged, scanned Rosie's appearance, nodded her approval, then turned Rosie around to face the mirror.

When Rosie saw her reflection all questions died on her lips. She could hardly believe what she was seeing. Arabella's evening gown was so flattering on her, with its pinched-in waist, sleeveless top and low-cut neckline. Rosie had never looked more beautiful.

She gave a small twirl and watched the gorgeous silver material spread out around her, its embroidered threads shimmering as they caught the light. She stopped and smiled at her reflection, gently touching the side of her head.

Nellie definitely had a magic touch when it

came to hairstyles. She turned her head from side to side and admired the transformation. It was easy to see why so many of the New York society ladies were determined to lure Nellie away from Arabella.

She looked down at the beautiful gown, still smiling, then a shadow of doubt crossed her mind and she frowned slightly.

'Do you think I'm perhaps showing a bit too much flesh?' She pulled up the plunging neck of the gown, only to have her hand swatted away by Nellie.

'Nonsense. It looks wonderful. And it took me hours to iron all that material, so we're not changing now.'

'Has anyone ever told you you're a very impertinent maid.'

'Yes, Arabella has, many times. And I take as much notice of her as I do of you. Now, m'lady, shall we put on a bit of rouge?'

Rosie batted at Nellie's arm with her gloves. 'Less of the "m'lady", thank you. And, no, I don't want any rouge.'

Rosie had blushed more since she had arrived at Knightsbrook than she had in the rest of her twenty years combined. The last thing she needed was any help to make her cheeks even redder.

'In that case I think you're done. I've been told

my services as your chaperon won't be required tonight. So off you go.'

'Mmm…' Rosie replied absentmindedly, still admiring her dress and her exquisite hairstyle. 'So what will you be doing to occupy yourself? Flirting with the footman or flirting with the coachman?'

'There won't be no flirting,' Nellie said, handing Rosie her fan. 'I went exploring the house while you were wandering round the garden, and I discovered the most wonderful library. I wouldn't want all those books to go to waste, would I? Plus, the Duke's valet is a bit of a bookworm himself, so he might be hiding out there tonight.'

Rosie smiled. 'So you'll be indulging in your two favourite pastimes? Flirting and reading.'

Nellie spent all her free hours back in New York in Mr van Haven's library—which was more than Mr van Haven himself did. He had bought the books in a mortgage sale because he had heard that a gentleman always had a library, but he'd never had any intention of actually reading any of them himself. He took as dim a view of reading as he did of all other art forms.

'Well, they're a bit difficult to do at the same time, but I'll try my best. After all, a bit of harmless flirting never hurt anyone,' Nellie said. 'And I imagine you'll be doing a bit of flirting yourself tonight.'

'Of course I won't. I don't flirt. I *never* flirt.'

That was she had never flirted before—had never wanted to. But then she had never met a man like Alexander before. Suddenly she could see the attraction of fluttering the occasional eyelash or doing a bit of pouting.

Soon she'd be seeing him again, and she'd be attired in a dress just made for flirting...

Soon she'd be seeing him again.

The thought hit her like a thunderbolt. Her stomach turned a series of somersaults and her chest constricted as if Nellie had tied her bodice laces too tight.

She wanted to see Alexander again, but felt ridiculously jittery at the prospect. This was not how she should be feeling. She wasn't here to flirt with the Duke. She wasn't supposed to have any feelings whatsoever for the Duke. She was here to make sure he had no interest in marrying Arabella, and she'd already achieved that. Now she just had to get these foolish emotions under control. Emotions she should not be feeling.

But how was she supposed to tell her heart to stop beating so fast? To stop her stomach from jumping every time his name was mentioned?

Rosie breathed deeply, her hand on her stomach in an attempt to calm her riotous body. Her body was refusing to listen to reason.

Alexander FitzRoy, Duke of Knightsbrook,

was not for her, she reminded her foolishly pounding heart. He didn't want to marry Arabella, the daughter of a fabulously wealthy man. He didn't want to marry Lydia, who was from a well-connected wealthy family. Under normal circumstances he wouldn't even *look* at someone like Rosie.

So just settle down, she ordered her jittering nerves. A command her nerves chose to ignore.

'Well, stop staring at yourself,' Nellie said. 'Go on, then. Get moving. You're the guest of honour—they'll all be waiting for you.' Nellie gave her a gentle nudge towards the door.

'Oh, well, here goes nothing,' Rosie said, adopting her bravest demeanour.

She took hold of the door handle, then stopped, as if incapable of turning it. This was not like her. She gripped the door handle more tightly. This was ridiculous, she admonished herself. She had no reason to feel nervous. It was all settled. She would not be marrying the Duke. He didn't want to marry her. She didn't want to marry him. There was nothing to worry about. All she had to do was enjoy a lavish dinner at a beautiful country estate. Perfect.

So why was she finding it so hard to actually leave her room?

'Go on—away with you,' Nellie said, removing her hand and turning the handle for Rosie. 'And mind you be careful. Don't complicate things even further by doing something stupid and going and falling in love with the Duke.'

Rosie rolled her eyes. 'As if I would.'

She left the room and headed down the corridor, with Nellie's words still ringing in her ears like an ominous warning bell.

Chapter Eight

'You can stop staring at the door, Alexander,' the Dowager Duchess said, and gave a little laugh. 'Your future fiancée will be here soon.'

Alexander sighed with exasperation. 'I'm not staring at the door, Mother.' He turned from the door and surveyed the other guests having pre-dinner drinks in the drawing room. 'And do I really need to repeat myself? We will not be getting married.'

'You can try and fool yourself, Alexander, but you can't fool your mother.'

'Arabella and I are in complete agreement: I do not want to get married and she does not want to marry me. The only person who wants this match is you, Mother.'

'Me, her father and your heart, Alexander.' She laughed and patted him lightly on the arm with her folded-up fan. 'I've seen the way you look at her. I've seen the way she looks at you. It's as if wedding bells start to chime every time you make eye contact.'

Alexander gave his mother a long, considered look. Such lyrical descriptions were not like her. It seemed the thought of getting hold of Arabella van Haven's generous dowry was making her poetic.

The door opened. Alexander and his mother turned to see who was being announced. A sense of disappointment swept through him as one of his mother's elderly friends entered the room.

Quashing down that ridiculous reaction, he turned to face his mother. 'Despite the noises you're hearing in your fevered imagination, we are *not* getting married, so let that be an end to it.'

'We'll see, Alexander. I'm sure before this weekend is over we will be announcing your engagement.'

'Mother, there will be no such announcement. You can put that idea right out of—'

He was interrupted by the footman announcing Miss van Haven's arrival.

Alexander turned and saw Arabella standing in the doorway. She looked stunning. And stunned was exactly how he felt. Her day dress had covered her from her neck to her toes, but in her evening gown he was treated to the sight of the creamy skin of her neck, her arms and a tempting décolletage. Her hair was no longer covered by a hat, and he could see it was not raven-black as he had first thought, but had copper threads running through it, which glimmered as they caught the light.

He swallowed to try and relieve his suddenly dry throat and could almost hear those bells his mother had alluded to. He shook his head to chase away such fanciful ideas.

Pull yourself together, man.

She looked in his direction and gave him a small, shy smile. At least it appeared to be a shy smile. Alexander wondered if he had been mistaken. A shy smile was not what he would expect from a young woman as confident as Arabella. Nothing about her suggested shyness. And yet she was still standing in the doorway, still looking in his direction from under lowered lashes, still with that small smile on her lips.

Perhaps the events of this afternoon had unnerved her after all. She had disguised her discomfiture at Lady Beaufort's outburst well, but perhaps she had not been unaffected. And now she had to face a room full of strangers—strangers who no doubt had been gossiping about her all afternoon.

No wonder she looked uncomfortable, and he was a fool to think it had anything to do with him.

Alexander stepped towards Arabella, but was stopped by his mother's hand firmly grasping his arm. 'Don't look so anxious, Alexander, or so desperate. I shall look after our guest.'

'I am neither anxious nor desperate, Mother. I merely intend to be polite.'

'Yes, Alexander, I'm sure that's all it is. Well, go and "be polite" to some of our other guests. I want to talk to my future daughter-in-law.'

'She's not—'

His mother walked away and joined Arabella at the doorway, placed her arm through hers and began leading her around the room, so she could exchange a few polite words with each of her fellow guests.

Arabella appeared to be chatting politely, and his fears that she was nervous about how the other guests would receive her following Lady Beaufort's scene abated. She looked completely unfazed as she walked around the room, confidently and majestically.

If things had been different she would indeed have made an excellent duchess and would have done the family name credit.

Shocked by that ridiculous thought Alexander headed for the sideboard, poured himself a brandy and knocked it back.

He looked over at Arabella again. She looked in his direction and once again sent him a small, seemingly shy smile, contradicting her otherwise confident manner. He refused to read anything into those smiles. He was the only person she knew. Of course she would be smiling at him. And if Thomas Gardener was here, no doubt her smiles would all be reserved exclusively for that man.

Alexander knocked back a second brandy and leant against the sideboard, determined not to speculate on what this Thomas Gardener might be like. Arabella had said he was "just a man"— but he was a man with whom she was in love. That made him a lot more than *just a man*.

He poured yet another brandy and swirled the rich brown liquid around the bottom of the glass balloon. No, he would *not* speculate about him. He placed the glass back on the sideboard with a decisive clink. Nor would he think about those shy smiles that Arabella was sending in his direction.

His mother had led Arabella to the corner where Charlotte was standing, her face a blank expression of boredom. She was pretending— not too convincingly—to listen to Lady Richmond, Dowager Duchess of Pemborne, who was no doubt retelling the story of her daughter's success during last year's season. Charlotte found their mother's parties even more dreary than he did, and he felt for his sister, who had fewer opportunities than he to escape the stultifying atmosphere.

The two young women bobbed curtseys and then Arabella took Charlotte's arm, leading her to a seat by the fire. Whatever she was saying to Charlotte, it was eliciting some surprising reactions from his usually serious sister. Charlotte's eyes grew wide. She bit her lip and then smiled slightly, as if she were doing something almost sinful.

As Arabella continued to talk Charlotte's smile grew wider, less guarded, and then she covered her mouth and laughed. Then, much to Alexander's amazement, she began talking animatedly, gesticulating wildly with her arms. When Charlotte finished what she was saying the two women laughed loudly, causing heads to turn in their direction. Remarkable.

'Damn fine woman you've got there.'

Alexander hadn't realised that Lord Darby was standing beside him.

'Yes, indeed,' he answered, before fully taking in what Darby had said. Arabella was *not* his woman.

'And I hear she's an heiress to boot. Capital. You can't go wrong with beauty and money.' The man gave a small chuckle and helped himself to a large brandy.

Alexander felt his nostrils flare as he fought to stifle his rising anger. Wasn't this exactly what he'd expected when his mother had suggested he marry an American heiress? That everyone would assume the marriage was a way for the FitzRoys to save their estate? That they had found an easy and convenient way to get out of debt?

'I have no interest in Arabella van Haven's fortune,' Alexander said through gritted teeth.

'Of course you don't, old boy. Marry for love… that's the ticket.' His Lordship winked as if they were sharing a private joke, slapped him on the back, and, smiling, walked off drinking his brandy.

Alexander looked over at Arabella. That was what everyone would think if he did marry Arabella. That he had married her for her dowry. The proud name Knightsbrook, which had been so tarnished by his father and his grandfather, would be further sullied. And that was something he would not do. He wanted to restore the name—not degrade it further.

It was good that Arabella was not interested in marriage to him. It was good that she was in love with another man—this Thomas Gardener. It made things simple. They would not be marrying. And that meant there was no need for him to get annoyed by comments made by men like Lord Darby.

But Lord Darby was certainly right about one thing. Arabella was most definitely a beautiful woman. She had an enchanting natural grace and ease of manner. And he had never met a woman who enjoyed herself so much. Her joyfulness seemed to infect everyone she met.

When was the last time he had seen Charlotte laugh and look so relaxed? It was hard to remember. And she certainly never laughed at a party hosted by his mother. A scowl or a look of resigned boredom were her more common expressions. Yet here she was, talking and laughing with Arabella as if they were already the best of friends. Yes, she was a beautiful woman, with a rare beauty that went beyond her pretty face.

The gong rang for dinner and Alexander strode over to the fireplace. 'May I accompany the two most attractive women in the room in to dinner?'

Charlotte smiled and stood up, but before she could take his arm Nicholas Sinclair, Lord Richmond, the errant son of his mother's best friend, was at Charlotte's side, bowing and offering his arm.

Nicholas had recently inherited the title Duke of Pemborne and his own vast estate, but the responsibility had done nothing to subdue his intemperate behaviour.

Charlotte stared up at Nicholas and could not suppress her look of disapproval, but good manners prevailed and with a resigned sigh she took his arm. Alexander had no doubt that Charlotte would have no interest in such a man—one whose reputation as an idle rake was as legendary as Charlotte's for being sensible and serious.

Arabella placed her hand lightly on his arm. 'It looks like Charlotte has made a conquest.'

Alexander scowled as Charlotte and Nicholas walked away together. 'I very much doubt if Charlotte would want to conquer a reprobate like him.' He made no attempt to keep his voice low, not caring whether Nicholas heard his low opinion or not.

They joined the procession into the dining room.

'You and Charlotte seemed to be enjoying yourself,' Alexander said, curious to know how she had managed to get Charlotte to laugh so freely.

'Your sister has a delightfully dry sense of humour.'

Alexander looked down at Arabella. He had heard many characteristics attributed to his sister—compassion for the less fortunate, a studious nature and a quick intelligence. But a sense of humour, dry or otherwise…? No, he hadn't heard that before.

'What were you two talking about?'

Arabella gave a tinkling laugh. 'Don't worry—we weren't talking about you.'

They arrived at their assigned places and the footmen pulled out their chairs.

'We were talking about the season and the extremes mothers go to in finding suitable husbands for their daughters.'

Alexander nodded, surprised that his sister should find anything in that banal tradition to laugh at. 'For Charlotte the season is something to be endured, not enjoyed. Mother has had to drag her kicking and screaming to the few balls she's attended this season, and I doubt if she'll attend any more.'

'Maybe she won't have to. His Grace seems quite taken with her.'

Alexander looked down the table to where Nicholas was sitting next to his sister, whose stern countenance and stiff posture did not support Arabella's assumption. 'I think a snowball has more chance in hell than Nicholas, Lord Richmond, has of wooing my sister. A more unlikely beau I can hardly imagine.'

'Hmm… I guess we'll have to wait and see.'

He looked at Arabella, who was wearing a knowing smile. He had no desire to inform her again that she was completely wrong. He knew his sister well. She most certainly would not be interested in a notorious rake like the new Lord Richmond. They might have been friends once, but that had been a long time ago. They had since grown into adults who could not be more different.

And why should it matter to Arabella anyway?

He took hold of his napkin before the footman could reach it, shook it vigorously and placed it on his lap. In the highly unlikely event that something should develop between Charlotte and Nicholas, Arabella would be long gone. Out of their lives and back to New York—back to Thomas Gardener.

Chapter Nine

Rosie looked down the table at Charlotte and smiled to herself. Alexander's sister was trying hard to act as if she wasn't interested in Nicholas, Lord Richmond, but nothing could disguise the flush on her cheeks or the quick, shy glances she kept flicking in his direction. They were obvious signs that she was interested. More than interested. She was attracted to her dashing companion.

Rosie touched her own warm cheeks. That was due to the heat coming from the many candles in the silver candelabra that adorned the centre of the dining table. It had nothing to do with Alexander. Nothing at all. And it certainly had nothing to do with what Nellie had said about the way she and Alexander had been looking at each other. Dewy-eyed, indeed.

She did not get dewy-eyed. Had never got dewy-eyed over any man. And she was certainly not going to get dewy-eyed over a man she couldn't have.

Rosie blinked several times to make sure her eyes were completely free of all dew.

At least one body part wasn't reacting inappropriately to Alexander sitting beside her. The same could not be said of her skin, her heart, her stomach… And her toes seemed to have curled themselves inside her silk evening slippers. And the least said about the strange tightening that was happening in her lower regions the better.

'You're very quiet, Arabella. That's not like you,' Alexander said as a footman began ladling soup out of silver tureens into porcelain bowls. 'What are you thinking about?'

Rosie blinked again, rapidly, and her mind went blank. She could hardly answer his question truthfully. She couldn't tell him she was taking an inventory of her various body parts, all of which were reacting in such a peculiar and disturbing way to being in such close proximity to him.

'Um…oh, nothing, really. I was just thinking how lovely the table setting is and how beautiful the women look in the candlelight.' Rosie released her breath, pleased that she hadn't blurted out something completely inappropriate.

The table did look wonderful, with an artful centrepiece of delightfully scented flowers, crystal glasses and silverware reflecting the candlelight, and the gilt mirrors adorning the walls shone with light to give a sense of intimacy. And the women seated around the long oval table, dressed in the lastest fashions, added to the sense of opulence. Their wealth was displayed in the diamonds, rubies, emeralds and other precious jewels that adorned their necks, wrists, ears and hands.

'None looks as lovely as you, Arabella. You look beautiful tonight. That colour suits you.'

Rosie's heart seemed to stop beating, and her breath caught in her throat as she took in the implication of what he had just said.

Beautiful...he thinks I'm beautiful.

An explosion of intense heat suddenly rushed to her face. Her stilled heartbeat sprang back to life, hammering furiously within her chest. A tingling pleasure coursed through her body and she smiled with unbridled joy. She did indeed feel beautiful. Nellie had worked magic on her hair, and Arabella's dress, with its cinched waist and plunging neckline, was designed to flatter her figure.

Tonight she felt every inch the society lady— almost as if this was where she belonged.

She had once lived a privileged existence. As a child she'd had expensive clothes, a room full of toys, and had been indulged by a loving mother and father. She had thought her life would always be like that. But then everything had changed. Her father had lost all his money. Her lovely mother had been reduced to working as a governess, and Rosie had become dependent on the reluctant charity of Mr van Haven and the kindness of Arabella.

Arabella did her best to ensure she never felt as if she was anything less than her equal, but her lack of money and security was something Rosie was always aware of.

However, tonight she was like Cinderella at the ball, seated next to her handsome prince, and it felt wonderful.

And, more than that, Alexander had noticed her appearance. He was still noticing—still looking at her—and under his gaze she felt as if she had dressed exclusively for him, so he would look at her, admire her, even desire her.

Alexander looked every bit the dashing Duke, dressed in a black dinner jacket, with a crisp white shirt and tie contrasting with his olive skin. Every man at the table was similarly attired, but Alexander wore it so much better. But then, a Greek athlete would, wouldn't he?

Rosie breathed in deeply, then exhaled slowly through pursed lips. 'Thank you, Alexander,' she murmured, feeling strangely tongue-tied as once again she reminded herself not to think of those naked Greek statues.

When he gazed back at her with those dark brown eyes her cheeks burned even hotter, her heartbeat pounded faster and her breath came in quicker and shallower gasps. Rosie was sure if her cheeks got any hotter she would ignite the table setting. She had to get herself under control.

Stop it...stop it right now, she admonished her traitorous body. A polite compliment should not make her feel this way. It should not cause her face to burn, and her skin to tingle as if it was being lightly caressed, or that disconcerting tightening between her thighs.

She moved slightly on her chair to try and release the tension that was gripping her, then coughed, pulled off her gloves and laid them beside her plate. She picked up a silver spoon and took a tentative sip of her mock turtle soup.

These strange reactions had to stop. Right now. It did not matter whether Alexander thought she looked beautiful or not. She looked the part. That was all that was important. She was fitting in with the elegant women at the table. Whether or not she looked beautiful to Alexander was of no matter.

She paused, her spoon halfway to her mouth. But he *did* think she was beautiful. A man like Alexander FitzRoy, Lord Ashton, Duke of Knightsbrook, thought she was beautiful.

No man had ever said that to her. Usually men didn't even look at her. On the odd occasion when she was allowed to appear at one of Mr van Haven's gatherings it was always made obvious that she was just the ward, a woman of no account, and all the men present treated her as such. She had never felt beautiful before.

Rosie sipped her soup although she tasted nothing, her mind awhirl, her body agitated.

She was being ridiculous—she had to get herself under control. So he'd called her beautiful? It meant nothing. In two days she would be back in London and this would all be over. She would not be marrying a handsome duke. The only reason she was seated at this table was because the Dowager Duchess thought she was an heiress and a good catch for her son—which she most decidedly was not.

'So, have you told your mother yet that we will not be getting married?' Rosie asked, reminding herself of her reason for being at this dinner table as much as asking a question.

'Repeatedly. But, as I've said, she's a very determined woman.

'Perhaps I need to start misbehaving again so she realises just how inappropriate a duchess I would make?'

Alexander looked at her over his wine glass and sent her a smile. And, oh, what a smile. It lit up his face and made those dark brown eyes shine with warmth. Warmth that sent shivers of delight coursing through her already agitated body.

Oh, yes, that was a sight Rosie hoped to see much more of.

'What do you plan to do? Throw some of the wine glasses against the wall? Or perhaps you could swipe the table clear and send the dinner service crashing to the ground?'

'Why, Your Grace, I do believe you're teasing me!' Rosie laughed. 'I am capable of misbehaving in many other ways.'

'That, I believe,' he said, still smiling that heart-stopping smile.

'I thought I might do a dance down the middle of the table. Do you think that would convince the Dowager that I'm not duchess material?'

Alexander nearly choked on his wine. 'I don't think even that would put my mother off. Unfortunately your father's fortune is so vast I suspect there's nothing you could do to offend her. Although I'd love to see you try. Shall I give you a hand up onto the table?'

Rosie swatted his arm lightly with her napkin. 'I'll save my table dance for the dessert course.'

The soup finished, the footmen removed their bowls and served the fish course, and Rosie reluctantly turned to talk to her other neighbour, as etiquette demanded. As he talked to her about the last shoot he had attended, and how many pheasants, ducks and other small creatures he had bagged, Rosie inclined her head in Alexander's direction and tried to hear what he was discussing with his own dinner companion.

To no avail. The murmur of the twenty-four people seated around the long oval dining table blocked out all voices but one—the man sitting beside her, boasting of his prowess with a shotgun.

The fish plates were removed and replaced with the meat course. With relief, Rosie turned back to Alexander. Her heart gave a little flutter when he smiled, suggesting that he too was pleased to be talking to her once again.

A *flutter*? She reminded herself that she was not supposed to be having a flutter, but she was incapable of suppressing it.

Especially when he continued to smile at her. A smile that was made more special because it happened so rarely. A smile that was even more of a treat because it was directed at *her*.

'I hope you're not going to tell me how many things you've killed lately?' She smiled back at him.

He shook his head in question. 'Killed?'

'My other dinner companion has just been telling me about all the ducks and pheasants whose lives he has prematurely snuffed out.'

'I see. No, I don't take part in the shoot. Nor do I ride to hounds.'

'Good. So, what was *your* other dinner companion talking about with such enthusiasm?' Rosie leaned forward and looked at the attractive blonde woman sitting to his left. Her smile faded and her jaw clenched before she forced herself not to be so ridiculous.

Why do I feel jealousy over a man who is not mine—who will never be mine?

'I don't know about enthusiasm, but she knew my father. She was lamenting that he had been missed at Royal Ascot last season and asking if I'll be taking his place this June.'

'Royal Ascot?'

'The race course. My father was very fond of gambling. *Too* fond of gambling.' He stabbed at a green bean, his smile disappearing. 'That's why the estate is in such a sorry mess.'

Rosie looked up from the impaled bean. 'Oh, so I take it you won't be attending Royal Ascot?'

'No, I won't.'

He cut up his roast beef with such vehemence Rosie almost felt sorry for it.

'I certainly will not be squandering what little funds we have left at the races.' He stilled his knife and drew in a deep breath. 'But there's no point getting angry about that. It's all in the past.'

Rosie nodded her agreement. Like him, she

tried hard—*very* hard—not to focus on the sorrows of the past, or to worry about what the future might bring.

Sometimes that could be hard. Sometimes memories of her mother and father came crashing in when she least expected it. Sometimes the vulnerability of her situation would overwhelm her. But then she would push that thought away and keep smiling. Even if sometimes that smile was not always as genuine as she would like it to be.

She had decided when she was still quite young that if she couldn't change the past, and the future was uncertain, then the present was the only time worth focusing on. And right now, sitting here, next to this handsome man, the present was rather pleasant.

'What about you, Arabella? Do you or your father like "a flutter"—as gamblers so innocuously describe losing a fortune at the card table, casino or race course?'

Rosie stilled her knife and fork and thought for a moment. Getting involved with Mr van Haven had been a gamble—a gamble her father had lost. He had once been a wealthy man. A successful engineer, he had built up a thriving company, installing modern electrical lighting in more progressive towns and businesses. His life had been comfortable. He had been married to the woman he loved, and living a contented life.

That was until Mr van Haven had encouraged him to borrow more money, to vastly expand his business throughout the country. When a few ventures hadn't worked out, and he hadn't been able to make his loan repayments, like a shark circling its prey, Mr van Haven had moved in. He had taken possession of the business and merged it with his own considerable portfolio.

Rosie's father had died prematurely, a broken man. As a supposed act of charity Mr van Haven had hired Rosie's mother as a governess and allowed Rosie to live in the house as a playmate for his daughter. Then her mother had died, leaving Rosie alone in the world.

She shuddered and blinked away the tears she would not shed. She did not want to dwell on such misfortune. And, anyway, it wasn't *her* father Alexander was asking about. It was Arabella's.

'No, I never gamble—and neither does my father. All he does is work. And when he wants to relax he works even harder. I can't imagine him doing something so frivolous as gambling, and he most certainly would never squander money.'

'It's an example I wish my father had followed.' Alexander lifted his glass to the invisible Mr van Haven and took a sip of red wine. 'But if he's working all the time I doubt you see much of him?'

Rosie nodded at the understatement. Mr van

Haven saw virtually nothing of Arabella. She suspected that was one of the reasons Arabella had argued with such passion to have Rosie taken on as his ward after Rosie's mother had died. Otherwise Arabella would have been left alone in that enormous house on Washington Square, with only her new, rather stern governess for company.

Mr van Haven was rarely at home, and when he was he was buried away in his study. He had little idea of what went on in the house. The girls were often left with minimum supervision, and over the years their friendship had grown and intensified, so they were now closer than many sisters.

Arabella's own mother had died not long after Arabella was born, and Rosie's mother had been more like a mother to her than a governess. When Rosie's mother had also died, Arabella had argued with her father, had thrown tantrums and threatened to run away, until Mr van Haven had finally relented and taken the fourteen-year-old Rosie as his ward.

'You're right. I see very little of my father. He's too busy making more and more money—as if no amount of money can ever be enough,' Rosie answered, as she imagined Arabella would.

'That must be very hard for you?'

She shrugged. 'Perhaps. But there are worse things in life than living in luxury with your every need catered for.'

That was something Rosie was well aware of. Thanks to Arabella, she did live in luxury, and did have her every need catered for. Without Arabella it might have been so different. She might have learnt first-hand what it was like to live in abject poverty, to be cold, to go hungry, to be vulnerable and alone.

Alexander took another sip of his red wine and gave her a considering gaze. 'That's true, but I suspect it is only your material needs that are catered for,' he said softly.

Rosie held his gaze, unable to look away. It was as if he were looking into her very soul and seeing the pain that she tried hard to bury, the past hurts she tried to forget, the vulnerability she hid behind a sunny smile.

'Oh, Arabella, I didn't mean to upset you,' he murmured.

His hand moved across the table and gently covered hers. It was a feather-light touch on her naked skin, but it sent a burst of fire coursing up her arm, consuming her in its blaze. She looked down at her small hand, covered by his strong, elegant fingers. That tender gesture had ignited a tempest within her—a tempest she felt incapable of quashing. She looked back at him. His dark eyes burned into hers and she gasped in a quivering breath as her body pulsated to the rapid beat of her heart.

The voices of the assembled guests seem to fade away. It was as if they were alone, no longer under the scrutinising gaze of society, and she longed for him to do more than just touch her hand—longed for him to take her in his arms so she could feel the strength of his body against her own. She ached to be held in those powerful arms, to give herself to his strong body, to have him complete her.

They held each other's gaze. Rosie hadn't noticed till now, but his dark brown eyes contained small gold flecks, like the last rays of sun on a summer's day. When she'd first seen him she had thought his eyes had a dark intensity, as if they absorbed all light. But she had been wrong. They contained warm lights. And now those lights were drawing her in, making her feel safe and protected.

She could gaze at those lovely warm eyes for ever…drown in them…forget everything else…

As if emerging from a trance she blinked several times and slowly slid her hand from underneath his. With shaking hands she took a sip of her wine, clutching the delicate stem of her glass as if it provided a lifeline back to reality, away from such fanciful thoughts.

She gave a light laugh that sounded false even to her own ears. 'No, you didn't upset me. As I've said before, I'm much stronger than I look.'

* * *

Her smile was false. There could be no doubt about that. And Alexander could hear sadness in her attempt at cheerfulness. He wanted to comfort her, to drive away that sadness behind her happy smile and her sunny disposition, to take her in his arms and make her safe.

'So what has made you so strong, Arabella?' he asked quietly.

'Oh, you know… I guess it comes from having a father who grew up in poverty. It puts iron in the soul.'

She took another sip of her wine and he could see her hand was shaking slightly, making a lie of her flippant response. He resisted the almost overwhelming urge to take hold of those trembling fingers. But she was not his to comfort—would never be his.

'I can tell you are a strong woman, Arabella. But even the strong need people to care for them and support them.'

She lowered her wine glass and looked up at him, her deep blue eyes capturing his gaze, capturing *him*. He couldn't have looked away even if he'd wanted to, and he didn't want to.

He had only known Arabella for one short day, but it was as if they had connected on a level he had not thought possible. He didn't know what it was that drew him to her. Was it her laughter, or the sadness in her eyes? Was it her vulnerability, or her resilience? Whatever it was, there was something infinitely attractive about this complex young woman—something that was drawing him to her.

'And is it the same for you, Alexander? Do you need someone to care for you and support you?' she asked, her voice barely a whisper.

Alexander shook his head, dismissing the idea. He had never expected support. After all, it was he who supported other people.

He had provided seemingly endless support for Lydia. She was a woman who knew only how to take, not to give. She had taken money to fund her gambling habit and taken from him emotionally, leaving him drained, with nothing left to give. He had thought he loved Lydia, but look where love had led him. And when she had finally left he'd known the only way to protect himself from such emotional demands was never to allow himself to get into such a position again.

So, yes, he had to be strong. He had his family to support, plus the tenants who all depended on him.

But in Arabella's eyes he could see such compassion, such warmth, such tenderness. He could imagine what it would be like to have such a woman by his side. A woman who would not only support him, but was also beautiful, delightful and captivating.

He shook his head again to drive away that fanciful idea. It didn't matter how beautiful Arabella van Haven was—she was in love with another man.

He gave a false laugh of his own. 'And is that what you offer Thomas Gardener? Your support?' Alexander could hear the bitterness in his voice and mentally chastised himself for such pettiness.

Arabella blushed a deeper shade of pink and took another sip of her wine, seemingly reluctant to discuss it.

'I should like to think that the man I love would always know he could rely on me to be by his side.'

She continued to toy with the stem of her wine glass. Once again her words seemed a contradiction of the emotion she was expressing. It was such a loving, positive statement, and yet she looked so sad—as if it was something she would like but knew would not happen.

Slowly she raised her gaze and looked into his eyes. For a moment he could almost believe she had been talking about *him*. The softness in those blue eyes spoke of a depth of emotion that almost left Alexander breathless.

He gripped his own wine glass tightly, to stop

his hand from reaching out and caressing her soft cheek. His gaze moved from her eyes to her lips—full pink lips which parted slightly under his gaze. Like him, she was taking in quick breaths, and she leaned in towards him as if mesmerised.

If only they were alone… Then he could do more than just gaze at that beautiful face.

The discreet cough of a footman drew him out of his trance and he saw the dessert course being placed on the table. Alexander waved the plate away and with the greatest reluctance turned towards his other dinner companion.

He hardly heard a word Lady Aubrey said. All he could think of was how Arabella had looked at him. Desire had sparked in her crystal blue eyes. Her lips had parted invitingly, as if waiting for his kiss. Like him, she seemed to have lost herself, forgotten who she was…

He had claimed he was strong and he was going to have to be. He could not succumb to temptation. She belonged to another man. *That* was what he had to think about when he looked at her—not how her raven hair caught the light, nor how plump her full lips were, nor how beautiful she looked when she sent him those shy smiles from under lowered lashes.

Quaffing a long draught of his wine, he reminded himself yet again. *She belongs to someone else.*

* * *

The dessert plates were removed and cheese and fruit platters were laid out on the table. Rosie turned back to Alexander, her heart beating fast, hoping he would look at her again with such intensity, with such longing.

Instead he gave a small, polite nod. It seemed the sensitive man she'd glimpsed had once again disappeared beneath a stern, aristocratic exterior.

'So, what were we discussing?' Rosie asked, not really caring about words, just hoping he would once again look at her with affection and warmth.

'You mentioned that your strength comes from having a father who was born in poverty.'

'Oh, yes, so I did. But what about you, Alexander? Did you get your strength from your father or your mother?'

Alexander gave a sudden humourless laugh. 'I don't know if I'd describe either of them as *strong*. My father and grandfather thought only of their own pleasure. They thought the family coffers were bottomless and they could spend and spend without a thought to the future, or the future of the tenants who depend on the success of the estate for their livelihoods. My mother is much the same. She brought a sizable dowry with her when she married my father, but he soon managed to squander that. There was no love between them, which perhaps made it easier for her to live with such a man. Having had a loveless marriage herself, she has no reservations about trying to get me to marry a wealthy heiress. All she can see is a way to save the estate. Hence your presence here this weekend. And no doubt when she finally accepts that we are not going to wed she will be in pursuit of some other heiress to throw in front of me.'

Rosie's heart lurched, and the bubble of exhilaration inflated by that look finally burst.

Another heiress.

Maybe the next heiress his mother threw in front of him would be a real one—one who actually wanted to marry Alexander. Maybe she'd be someone Alexander was interested in. Maybe she'd be someone he *wanted* to marry.

She stabbed her cheese knife into a piece of Stilton. There was no 'maybe' about it. Eventually Alexander was going to meet someone he wanted to marry. Someone who wasn't just pretending to be an heiress. Her prodding reduced the wedge of Stilton to a pile of mush and she moved on to massacre a slice of Wensleydale.

But surely it would be a *good* thing if he met and married a real heiress. Surely she should want him to be happy. After all, she didn't want him to remain single, did she? He should find himself a wife—someone he could love and who would love him in return.

'Are you planning on eating that cheese, Arabella? Or are you just going to cut it into smaller and smaller portions?'

Rosie gave a small fake laugh. 'I think I've had enough.' She placed her knife down. Yes, she'd had enough food. And, more than that, she'd had enough of this play-acting and enough of being caught up in the moment and thinking she could mean something to Alexander.

She had felt like Cinderella at the ball, wearing her beautiful gown and sitting next to her handsome prince. But this was just another fairy tale—one she had foolishly allowed herself to think was reality. But in the real world the pauper didn't get the prince.

What did it matter how he gazed at her? What did it matter how often he touched her hand? What did it matter if he said she looked beautiful?

It didn't. And she was a fool to think otherwise.

A crushing heaviness suddenly descended on her, sweeping away the sense of lightness and excitement that came from talking and laughing with Alexander.

She had been trying to fool Alexander and his mother by pretending to be Arabella and she had succeeded, but in the process she had managed to fool herself. Fool herself that she could be part of this world, could have a man like Alexander really wanting her, little Rosie Smith, a no-account orphaned ward, with no money, no position—nothing. She didn't even own the beautiful gown she was wearing.

Yes, she had been a fool—a deluded fool.

All she wanted now was for this evening to end, so she could drop this pointless pretence and get back to reality. A reality that did not contain handsome but unattainable dukes or dreams that were far above her expectations.

Chapter Ten

'Ladies, shall we adjourn and leave the men to their port and cigars?' The Dowager stood up before anyone dared to answer her rhetorical question.

Footmen rushed forward to pull out the chairs of the assembled female guests and the women immediately fell into line, as if under orders from a commanding officer.

Rosie joined the brightly coloured trail of well-dressed woman exiting the room to the accompaniment of rustling silk and satin. Mixed emotions coursed through her as she left the dining room... left Alexander's side.

She wanted to spend more time with him, but knew she had to get away. Her behaviour during dinner had been inappropriate—and not in the inappropriate manner she had intended when she had concocted her plan over tea at the Ritz.

Instead of presenting herself as a thoroughly

unacceptable future bride she had been giving him long, lingering looks. Instead of making absurd and discourteous statements to prove what an unacceptable duchess she would make she had been sharing an intimate conversation with him. Instead of acting unimpressed and dismissive she had been getting all dewy-eyed, just as Nellie had said.

She had been acting like a woman who was being courted by a man she adored—a woman who was loving every minute of it. And, worst of all, it had not been an act. She had thoroughly enjoyed being in Alexander's company. Had loved the way he looked at her. Had loved him touching her…had wanted more, much more.

What was *wrong* with her? Her friend was depending on her. Her best friend. The friend who had saved her from a life of penury. The friend to whom she owed so much and for whom she claimed she would do anything. Was she such a terrible person that she would allow her head to be turned by a handsome man and forget her promise to her friend? It would seem so. There was only one reason for her visit to Knightsbrook House: to save Arabella from an unwanted marriage. Nothing else.

Rosie wanted to hang her head in shame. Instead she turned before she left the room, for one last look at Alexander. He smiled at her and her foolish heart did a somersault.

The door closed behind the train of women and Rosie shook her head slowly from side to side.

No, this would not do at all. She could not go on behaving like this. She was sending out all the wrong messages. It was time she stopped acting like an infatuated debutante at her first ball of the season. And if she couldn't trust herself with Alexander then it was best if she spent no more time in his company.

The women entered the drawing room, where coffee was being served. Rosie took a delicate white china cup from the parlour maid, sat beside the fire and sipped the rich, nutty drink. Charlotte soon joined her, flopping down in the adjoining wing chair and exhaling loudly.

'Thank goodness that's finally over. These dinner parties are always such a bore,' Charlotte said, and took a decisive bite of her Florentine biscuit.

'Really? You seemed to be enjoying His Grace's attention.' Rosie couldn't help herself. She had to tease the girl.

'No, I was not.' The quick and vehement reply made a lie of Charlotte's answer.

Rosie raised her eyebrows and Charlotte shrugged. There was obviously more to this story than Charlotte was telling.

'Nicholas and I were friends once, but he's

changed so much,' Charlotte said. 'All he cares about now is enjoying himself and chasing after—' Her cheeks reddened slightly and her lips pinched with disapproval. 'Chasing after women. He really is quite frightful—and he had so much promise when he was young.'

'But you still find him attractive?'

Charlotte shrugged and stared into the fire. 'Only his appearance is attractive. The things he does and the way he lives his life are anything but attractive.' She sat up straighter in her chair and turned to face Rosie. 'But what about you, Arabella? You and Alexander seemed to be completely absorbed in each other, talking quietly with your heads so close together they were almost touching.'

Rosie took another sip of her coffee while she composed her response. 'Your brother is an interesting conversationalist,' she said, in her most nonchalant manner.

Charlotte's eyes grew wide. 'Really? Alexander? Most of the ladies who attend Mother's dinner parties describe him as taciturn and complain that they can hardly get a word out of him. Not that I blame him. Who wants to spend an evening making small talk about the weather, the last ball they attended or the next ball they plan to attend? Certainly not me, and certainly not Alexander.'

She took another bite of her biscuit and chewed it thoughtfully while watching Rosie.

'So, if you weren't talking about the weather or this season's balls, what *were* you talking about?'

'Oh, I can't really remember. This and that.'

'It must have been a very interesting "this and that". I've never seen Alexander so engrossed in a conversation with a woman. Not since…' Charlotte took a sip of her coffee and looked into the fire, then back at Rosie. 'Not for a long time. And I can hardly remember the last time I saw him laughing. But when he's with you he seems to laugh and smile a lot. I think you're really good for him, Arabella.'

Rosie cringed at the sound of her friend's name. She was *not* Arabella. Whether Rosie made Alexander laugh or not was of no importance. In a few days she would be gone and would never see the FitzRoys again.

'So?' Charlotte said, looking down at her coffee cup and turning it round in the saucer. 'Were you and Alexander discussing your wedding plans?'

Rosie almost spluttered on her coffee. 'No, we weren't discussing *any* wedding plans. I'm afraid Alexander and I will not be getting married. We've discussed it, and neither of us wants it. It was a plan concocted by my father and your mother, without the approval of either of us.'

Charlotte's lips drooped into a pouting frown. 'But you seem to be getting on so well. You seem so right for each other. You were looking at each other as if…' She shook her head slightly and sighed. 'Can't you at least get to know each other a bit better before you decide? You might change your minds. My mother might, for once in her life, be right.'

Rosie shook her head. 'I'm sorry, Charlotte. It's not possible.' She could not tell this lovely young woman that it was impossible because she wasn't really Arabella.

Charlotte gave another heavy sigh and stared into the fire, her shoulders slumped.

Rosie doubted it was possible to feel any worse. This was not how her plan was supposed to work out. She was not supposed to actually *like* the FitzRoys. They were supposed to be a stuffy, snobby family, grasping after Mr van Haven's money. They were supposed to be people she would not have any qualms about making fun of. Instead the Duke was handsome and charming and his sister was a lovely young woman who was honest, trusting and extremely likeable.

The only person who was despicable was Rosie herself. Despicable for playing this trick on such good people, despicable for lying to Alexander, and despicable for not sticking to the plan she had agreed with the real Arabella over tea at the

Ritz. No, she couldn't feel much worse than she did right now.

Charlotte turned from the fire and gave Rosie a sad smile. 'But *we* can still be friends, can't we? Even if you don't marry Alexander?'

Rosie slumped in her chair. She had been wrong. It *was* possible to feel worse. Now she was going to have to lie to Charlotte.

She nodded her head and cringed inwardly. 'Of course we can.'

Another lie, to add to the long list of lies she had already told. Obviously she could not be friends with Charlotte after she left Knightsbrook, as they would never see each other again. And it was unlikely Charlotte would want to be friends with Rosie if she discovered the truth and found out that she had been so shamefully deceived.

'Good. And who knows? Maybe eventually you and Alexander will realise it's not such an impossible match after all and we'll be more than just friends. We'll be sisters!'

Rosie's inward cringe became an outward wince as she gritted her teeth and tried to smile through her embarrassment.

Smiling with satisfaction, Charlotte picked up her coffee cup, lifted it to her lips, then put it back in the saucer. 'I'm sorry, Arabella. I've just realised I'm behaving exactly like my mother. She wants you and Alexander to marry and she cares little for what you two want. And I'm doing exactly the same. I would love it if you got married, but obviously you have to make your own decisions and nobody should force you to do anything you don't want to do.'

'Thank you, Charlotte. But you have nothing to apologise for.'

And that was definitely the truth. If anyone should be apologising it was Rosie.

'But you don't need me putting on the pressure. You're going to have enough of that from Mother—and, believe me, she is a master at putting on the pressure.'

'Is she pressuring you to marry as well?' Rosie was curious to know, but also desperate to change the subject, away from herself and Alexander, or at least form Arabella and Alexander.

'Yes, it's already started.'

Rosie listened while Charlotte detailed the plans and schemes her mother was putting in place to try and get Charlotte married off to Nicholas, Lord Richmond. While Rosie commiserated, a small part of her was grateful that Charlotte was passionately diverted from discussing any future plans of Arabella and Alexander.

The drawing room door opened. Several men carrying brandy glasses entered along with the waft of cigar smoke. Full of bonhomie, they joined the ladies and the volume of conversation in the room rose markedly. Servants began arranging card tables and the lid of the grand piano was lifted. It seemed the party was not about to end any time soon, and a range of entertainments had been organised for the evening.

Rosie's stomach tightened as if the coffee had been far too strong. It seemed she would be expected to spend more time with Alexander, and to continue pretending for a while longer yet.

Her confusion mounted. What was it she was actually pretending to be? Was she pretending to be interested in Alexander, or not interested in him? Was she not interested, but pretending she was, or interested but pretending she wasn't?

Another smiling man entered the room and Rosie quickly looked up, her stomach clenching. It was not Alexander, and Rosie was both pleased and disappointed. She wanted to see him again, but knew it was wisest not to. And if she was going to avoid seeing Alexander now was the time to take action—because once he entered the room she was unsure whether she would have the willpower to walk away from him.

'I'm starting to get a slight headache,' Rosie told Charlotte—something which did have a kernel of truth to it. All this confusion over what she did and didn't want was starting to make her head spin. 'I'm also a little tired after such an eventful day.'

'Oh, of course—you must retire for the evening if you aren't well. But Mother will be disappointed. She was expecting you to give us a performance on the banjo tonight. She purchased one especially for the occasion.'

The banjo? Why on earth would the Dowager expect her to play the banjo? Rosie played the piano, not the banjo.

Then suddenly she remembered, and gave a small laugh.

'You *do* play the banjo, don't you, Arabella? You're looking somewhat surprised, but we were told you had been playing since you were a child and are quite brilliant.'

Both Rosie and Arabella had learnt the banjo briefly, when they were in their early teens, when they'd harboured dreams of running off and joining a group of travelling performers. But that dream had died a sudden death, as had so many of their outlandish youthful plans for travel and adventure, and the banjos had been consigned to the attic to gather dust.

Mr van Haven paid such little attention to his only child that he presumably thought Arabella had continued with her banjo lessons and had claimed it as one of her accomplishments.

'I afraid that is one talent I suspect has been

greatly exaggerated. So I think it might be best if I do retire early, if I'm to avoid ruining the evening and subjecting the guests to that particular torture.'

She bade Charlotte goodnight, then approached the Dowager, her brow furrowed with fictitious pain.

'I'm sorry, Your Grace, but all the excitement of the day and the journey has left me quite fatigued, and I can feel a terrible headache coming on.' She placed the back of her hand on her forehead to emphasise the point. 'My apologies, but I fear I must retire for the evening.'

It might be another lie, but it was in a good cause. She would be saving the guests from her lack of finesse on the banjo, not to mention saving herself from having to cope with the strange, tumultuous emotions that Alexander elicited in her.

The Dowager smiled and patted her arm. 'Of course, my dear. You must rest. Then you'll be fresh tomorrow. I know Alexander is very keen to show you the rest of the estate; he was talking about it earlier and quite bubbling with enthusiasm.'

Alexander? Bubbling?

It seemed Rosie wasn't the only one capable of stretching the truth.

'I'm sure no one bubbles quite like Alexander,' she couldn't stop herself from saying, before giving a tired smile, bobbing a quick curtsey and retreating as quickly as she could without looking too energetic.

The door closed behind her with a decisive click and she walked as quickly as decorum allowed down the tiled entranceway towards the staircase.

The dining room door opened, releasing a group of smiling men, all talking loudly. She nodded greetings as she passed, determined to escape before she saw Alexander again.

Reaching the staircase, she fought the temptation to run up the stairs. That would hardly fit in with her claim to be tired and have a headache coming on.

'Arabella, are you retiring early?'

His deep, velvety voice was behind her. She froze, then slowly turned to face him, her hand tightly gripping the bottom of the carved banister. He was standing at the dining room doorway, a brandy balloon in his hand, and Arabella's breath left her chest. He looked even more magnificent than when she had first seen him.

Was that even possible?

A shiver ran through her. Her hand clasped her stomach, to still the riotous storm of nerves that had erupted deep within her, and her gaze wandered over the sublimely handsome man staring back at her.

Yes, it seemed it was possible.

With his strong body filling the doorframe, he was a picture of masculine strength and virility. Rosie gasped in a quick breath and slowly exhaled as her gaze moved down his body to those long, lean legs, and the muscles delineated through the black fabric of his trousers. Oh, yes, her original assessment had been right. He was the very image of a Greek statue.

Her gaze moved back up to his face, to his dark brown eyes. Eyes that were sparkling with the reflected candlelight of the large chandelier. Eyes that were drawing her in and holding her tight with the intensity of his gaze. Part of her was frightened by the power of that gaze, but most of her wanted to surrender herself to the strong tidal pull that was sweeping her towards him.

She coughed lightly. 'Yes, I'm feeling a little tired, so I thought I'd retire.'

And I need to escape from you before I make even more of a fool of myself than I already have, she added truthfully to herself.

He placed the brandy glass on a nearby table, the amber liquid swirling in the balloon-shaped glass, and crossed the entranceway. 'Yes, you look pale, Arabella. Is there anything I can do?'

You can stop being so handsome. You can stop

being so charming. You can stop making my heart skip every time I see you. Then I wouldn't be looking so pale. Then I wouldn't be feeling so shocked at seeing you again.

'No, nothing. I think I just need an early night.'

'Then allow me to accompany you up to your room. Shall I call my sister to act as a chaperon?'

Rosie shook her head. 'No, don't disturb her. And there's no need to accompany me. Nellie will be waiting for me. She can see to my needs.'

Another lie. Only Alexander would be able to see to the need that was surging up within Rosie. A need to be taken in his arms. A need to be held by him. A need to feel those full, sculpted lips pressed against hers.

Rosie closed her eyes and blinked several times to try and clear that image from her mind. But when she opened her eyes she was staring straight at those sculpted lips…lips that were saying something…something that the pounding of her heart prevented her from hearing.

'I beg your pardon? What did you say?'

'I was offering you my arm so I can help you up the stairs.'

'Oh, yes. Of course.'

Rosie was sure that touching him right now was the worst thing she could do, but what could she say? *No, I don't want to take your arm? If I take your arm I don't think I'll be able to trust*

*myself not to do something so inappropriate that
even I'll be shocked by it?*

He held out his arm and Rosie drew in a series of steadying breaths. She commanded her
fingers to unclench themselves from the banister and lightly placed her hand on his forearm.

She briefly closed her eyes, registering the
touch of her skin on his muscular arm, and tried
to ignore the tingling sensation burning its way
up her arm to her chest and taking over her body.

As they ascended the stairs she could hear him
making polite conversation, but what he said she
had no idea. All she could do was react to the
closeness of his warm body and the wonderful
scent of him…pure, heady masculinity.

Rosie followed where he led, sure that if she
had been trying to find her way down the maze of
corridors with their array of paintings and sculptures adorning the walls she would have got completely lost, her mind was so befuddled.

They'd reached her door.

He paused, removed her hand from his arm and
took it in both of his. He smiled gently down at
her. 'It seems you are starting to feel a bit better,
Arabella. Colour has returned to your face,' he
said, his voice concerned.

Rosie didn't doubt that she was blushing—the
heat radiating from her burning cheeks was making that very clear. And it was not just her cheeks

that were burning. Rosie was sure her entire body must be blushing. It was pulsating fiercely as her heart thumped within her chest, as if she'd just undertaken some kind of furious exercise.

'Th-thank you,' she stammered, unsure what she was thanking him for.

'Well, I will leave you to your rest.'

But he remained staring down at her, once again capturing Rosie with the intensity of his brown eyes.

'Goodnight, then,' Rosie murmured, unable to move herself.

He lifted her hand and lightly kissed the back of it, his eyes still burning into hers. Rosie closed her eyes, loving the feeling of the touch of his lips on her skin. But she wanted more.

As if her hand had a mind of its own it turned over and lightly stroked his strong jawline. Her gaze moved to his lips. Those full, sensual lips. And she imagined what it would be like to be kissed by him.

Tingling erupted on her lips and she gave a small moan. She caught her bottom lip with her teeth, slowly raking them across the skin to stop any more tell-tale reactions.

Alexander's hand gently clasped her wrist. Their eyes locked. Heat surged through her as she registered the hunger in his dark eyes…a hunger both exciting and unnerving.

Time froze. Every inch of her body tensed as she waited for him to act. Her breath caught in her throat. She stared up at him, waiting to see what he would do next. Would he kiss her? Oh, how she wanted him to kiss her.

In answer to her silent plea his lips met hers, his kiss crashing over her like turbulent water escaping from a ruptured dam. As his skin rasped against her cheek she inhaled the lemon scent of his shaving soap. Then a stronger, underlying masculine scent and taste filled her senses like a powerful narcotic, taking her over, intoxicating her, leaving her incapable of thought.

But now was definitely not the time for thinking.

Her lips parted wider, to savour more of that musky masculine taste and the delicious hint of brandy. To her surprise his tongue entered her mouth. Was this how men and women kissed? It was her first time, so how could she be sure—but, oh, how good it felt.

His tongue continued to lick and probe, tasting her until she was sure she would collapse from the heady pleasure of having it so intimately inside her mouth. But she couldn't collapse—not with his arms holding her close, so close she could feel the muscular imprint of his strong chest against her breasts, feel his long, lean thighs against hers, feel his hard arousal against her stomach.

Rosie gasped, realising what was pressing against her, his unmistakable need for her.

What would happen now?

Rosie had no idea. She had often wondered whether a man would ever kiss her and, if so, if she would know what to do. But it seemed all she had to do was surrender herself to Alexander and he would guide her. With him to lead her she was free to give herself over to the wild, primitive need building up inside her. The insatiable need for *him*.

Tendrils of hair became dislodged from her carefully constructed coiffure, tumbling around her naked shoulders, intensifying that glorious sense of abandon.

Her tongue took a few tentative licks at his lips, then entered his mouth. Their tongues engaged in an erotic dual, causing him to release a soft moan of pleasure. Exhilaration surged through her. She had made him moan—moan for *her*. Oh, yes, this felt so right. She wanted more of this. Wanted to explore his strong masculine body...wanted to discover just how much pleasure she could experience and how much pleasure he could give her.

Encircling his neck, she ran her hands up through his thick brown hair. She growled with pleasure as his kiss deepened. Her body moved to its own rhythm as his hands ran down her spine, cupping her buttocks and pulling her firmly against his body.

Oh, yes, she definitely wanted more of this. She wanted him never to stop kissing her, never to let her go.

Without thinking, just reacting to the needs of her body, she rubbed her swollen breasts against his hard chest, her tight nipples pressing through the soft fabric of her gown and aching to be touched. To be touched by *him*.

His lips left hers, but her disappointment was quashed when he kissed a line slowly down her neck. Rosie tilted back her head, loving the touch of his lips on her exposed skin as every kiss sent waves of pleasure rippling through her body.

When he reached the base of her neck she mentally urged him to go further. His lips obeyed.

He slid the neckline of her dress off one shoulder, then the other, his lips kissing a tantalising line across her skin. Rosie's breath came in faster and faster gasps, her heart pounded loudly in her chest, and a throbbing pleasure erupted deep within her core.

'Oh, Arabella, you're so beautiful,' he murmured, then kissed her neck, his husky voice almost unrecognisable.

Rosie froze.

Arabella. He had called her Arabella.

She was not Arabella. She was Rosie Smith.

And what was she doing? Kissing a man who thought she was Arabella. She was tarnishing Arabella's good reputation. How could she *do* that? What sort of woman *was* she?

She closed her eyes and took a few deep breaths to bring herself back to reality. When she opened her eyes he too had changed. His posture had become rigid, his face stern. Her hesitation seemed to have broken the spell that had captured them both. He appeared to be emerging from a trance, as if he were suddenly registering just what they were doing.

'I beg your pardon, Arabella. Please forgive me.'

She shook her head. He had nothing to be sorry for. It was she who should be sorry. She was the one who had forgotten who she was—the one who had betrayed her best friend's good name.

He coughed, inhaled deeply, then released his breath slowly. 'I took advantage of you. I'm so sorry.'

She stared at him as if he were talking an unknown foreign language. What did he mean? Took advantage of her? How?

In a daze, she watched as he pulled up her dislodged neckline and retrieved her abandoned hairclips from the floor.

'Kissing you was unpardonable, but I hope you can one day forgive me?'

'No. I mean yes. I mean, you've done nothing that needs my forgiveness.'

Rosie touched her lips. That kiss had been the most wonderful thing that had ever happened to her. How could he say it was unforgivable?

He looked down at his hands, now clenched into fists around her hairclips. 'I have. I took advantage of you and I am sorry.'

Rosie shook her head again. He was so wrong. She had wanted him to kiss her. She still wanted him to kiss her. To hold her. To caress her. Even now that she knew it was wrong and could never happen again.

'My behaviour would be unforgivable under any circumstances, but it is especially reprehensible that I took advantage of a woman who is all but betrothed to another.'

What was he talking about? *All but betrothed?* Then with a sinking feeling she remembered Thomas Gardener. The non-existent Thomas Gardener. He thought he was betraying a non-existent man, when it was Rosie who was betraying a real person—her best friend, the friend who had saved her from poverty, the friend who had always treated her like a sister.

'Please, I implore you, do not feel you have in any way wronged me.'

'You are an admirable young woman, Arabella.

It seems that is another virtue to add to the long list.' He handed her the retrieved hairclips.

She took them from his outstretched hands and stared down at them as if unsure what they were, once again shamed by her actions. Admirable? Nothing about her was admirable. And if she actually did possess any virtues she couldn't think of a single one right now.

No, there was nothing admirable about the lies she had told him—was still telling him. Nothing admirable about what she had just done. To satisfy her own longings she had put her friend's reputation at risk. The only admirable person was the man standing before her, begging for her forgiveness.

And there was certainly nothing admirable about her wish that he would kiss her again. Even now—now that she realised just how wrong it had been—she still wanted it. How could she want something that was so wrong so badly? No, there was nothing admirable about Rosie Smith.

'Perhaps we should put it down to the heat of the moment,' she said, as much to excuse her own bad behaviour as to make him feel less remorseful. 'We must put it behind us and pretend it never happened.'

Although she knew that was yet another lie. There was no way she would ever forget the touch of Alexander's lips on hers, nor how it had felt to be encased in his arms. That feeling would stay with her for ever.

He bowed. 'You are very gracious. I wish you goodnight, Arabella.'

Graciousness—that was another virtue she doubted she actually possessed.

'Goodnight, Alexander,' she murmured.

She remained rooted to the spot, watching his back as he retreated down the corridor. When he disappeared around the corner she inhaled deeply and placed a steadying hand on her rapidly beating heart. She entered her bedroom, leaned against the closed door and slid to the floor, her body suddenly too heavy for her to remain standing.

With her head in her hands she vowed that it would never happen again. If she could not trust herself in the Duke's company she must never allow herself to be alone with him. *Ever.*

Chapter Eleven

That should not have happened. That most definitely should not have happened. What had he been *thinking*? That was the problem. He hadn't been thinking—just reacting.

He had felt so close to her over dinner. They had laughed together, talked together, shared a closeness that he had not felt for a long time, and it had affected his ability to reason clearly. And then, when he had seen her looking up at him, desire sparking in those big blue eyes, the last vestige of reason he'd possessed had been trampled under his need to take her in his arms.

He had ignored the small voice in his mind that had warned him it was wrong because he'd wanted her so much.

Alexander slammed shut the door and paced his bedroom floor. With his blood pumping, his body tense and his throbbing lust for Arabella straining his breeches, he desperately needed release from this pent-up desire. He had to free himself of this demanding need for her, for the feel of her, the taste and smell of her.

And that wasn't going to happen if he continued to think about what she'd looked like with her hair tumbling loose around her naked shoulders, her red lips wet and plump, her full breasts arching towards him invitingly and with that look in her eyes—a look that had mirrored his own insatiable desire.

No, it should never have happened. He should never have taken her in his arms. The moment he'd given in to that temptation he had been incapable of stopping, incapable of resisting the need to kiss her, to caress her warm, silky skin.

Balling his hands into tight fists at his sides, he tried to erase the feel of her, tried to chase away the fresh scent of spring flowers that still filled his senses, tried to drive out the image of her gazing up at him with hooded eyes, her lips parted, the mounds of her breasts rising and falling in her tight bodice as she waited for his kiss.

That he was falling for the beautiful Arabella van Haven there could be no denying. He slammed his fist against the wall. He was a fool—a damn fool. After Lydia's betrayal, the next woman he'd fallen for was someone betrothed to another. Was he a glutton for punishment? Had Lydia not hurt him enough with her lies, her tricks?

Because of Lydia he had vowed never to let a woman affect him ever again. But he had let his guard down because Arabella was not like Lydia. She didn't lie. She didn't deceive others for her own ends. She was an innocent young woman. And that only made his behaviour worse.

Lydia had been betrothed to him and had been seduced away by another. Now he had almost done to Arabella what that rake had done to Lydia. He had tried to have his way with a woman who was in love with someone else, who planned to marry someone else. At the time he had despised the man who had seduced Lydia, and yet now he had shown himself to be no better—to be just as much a reprobate as that man had been, a man driven only by his lust for a beautiful woman.

He paced backwards and forwards, rubbing his now bloodied hand, his breath coming in a series of rapid gasps.

Lydia had given herself to that man and followed him into a life of debauchery. Her position in society had been ruined for ever. And now *he* was set on ruining the reputation of a lovely young woman all because he'd wanted her so badly he had forgotten himself—had forgotten all sense of propriety, all sense of decency.

He could only be grateful that she had come to her senses and stopped him. Her sudden withdrawal from his touch had allowed the memory of her telling him that she was in love with another man to invade his fevered brain.

If she hadn't come to her senses he would have been incapable of stopping at just a kiss. He would have taken her to his bedroom and torn off her restricting clothing. He would have freed those enticing breasts, released the tight, sensitive nipples so he could take them in his mouth, kiss them, nuzzle them, lick them until she was senseless with lust for him.

She would now be lying beneath him, writhing under his touch as he kissed every inch of her body. Her legs would be wrapped tightly around his waist as she gave herself to him, opened herself up for him so he could enter her. She would be calling out his name, desperate for the pleasure he would give her, the pleasure she would give *him*.

He slammed his bloodied fist against the wall, leaving a red smear on the cream paper. Yes, he was a fool. A damn fool. He should not even be *thinking* such things. She belonged to another man. She was in love with another man. Yes, she had kissed him back. Yes, she had responded to his touch. But she was an innocent. It was he who should have known better than to take her into his arms. It was unforgivable.

He had been so desperate to satisfy his own consuming lust for her that all he had cared about was satisfying his own needs. But it wasn't just her body that was driving him mad with desire. He could not remember the last time he had enjoyed a woman's company more. Talking to her had made his mother's unbearable dinner party more than just bearable—it had been entertaining.

It was wrong—and yet for one moment it had felt so right. It had felt as if she was his. When she had been in his arms it had felt as if she belonged there, belonged to *him*. But it was not where she belonged. She was not his. She was in love with another man—all but betrothed to another man.

Explosive energy continued to pump through his veins. He would go mad if he remained in this room, pacing like a caged tiger.

With unnecessary force he pulled open his bedroom door and slammed it shut behind him. He had to get out of the house, out into the open. He needed to feel the cold night air on his face.

He ran down the stairs and out through the front door, ignoring the startled looks of the servants. He crossed the lawn, bathed in the soft light spilling out through the house's large windows, ripping off his jacket, his waistcoat and his shirt.

When he reached the lake he pulled off his boots and his trousers and tossed them to the ground. Naked, he dived in.

The cold water hit him like a punch—the punch he needed…the punch he deserved.

But the cold water was not enough to douse his burning lust for Arabella. He swam the length of the lake, his arms rapidly slicing through the water. When he reached the opposite edge he turned and swam back, again and again.

The lights from the house did not reach the lake, and the dark moonless sky made it almost impossible to see his way as he raced up and down in the inky black water. But he had swum this lake many times. He knew it so thoroughly he could navigate his way without sight, without thought. And that was what he needed. Not to think. To exhaust himself.

His body finally began to tire, but he pushed himself on, forcing himself to continue despite his fatigue. Finally, his energy completely spent, he came to a halt. He flicked the water out of his hair and held on to the stone paving at the edge of the lake, his breath coming fast, his heart thumping with the exertion.

He looked up at the house, now in complete darkness. While he'd been swimming the guests, his family and even the servants had all retired for the night. Arabella was no doubt now asleep.

An image of Arabella in her four-poster bed invaded his mind, with her long black hair spread out across a white pillow, her lithe body lying in repose. Her delicious curves would be visible through a linen nightdress…

He slapped at the water. Why did he have to think of that? Why did he have to torture himself? All that strenuous exercise had been for nought if it hadn't driven thoughts of Arabella from his mind.

He forced himself to swim one more length of the lake. Slowly he ploughed through the cold water, his muscles screaming out for him to stop. He reached the end, but his mind still reeled with images of Arabella.

This was insufferable. His fatigue was so intense that if he swum another length surely he would drown. It seemed if he was ever to be free he was going to have to exercise strenuous control over his mind, not just his body.

Summoning up every last ounce of strength, he dragged himself out of the lake, grabbed his trousers and pulled them over his wet body. He picked up his boots and crossed the lawn to retrieve his discarded shirt, waistcoat and jacket, now damp from the night-time dew. Slowly he retraced his steps up the path to the dark house, returned to his room and fell onto his bed in complete exhaustion.

He stared up at the ceiling and made a solemn vow. Even if the opportunity arose, and even if the temptation was overwhelming, he would not succumb to his feelings for Arabella van Haven. He would never again take her in his arms. Never again would he kiss her. He would exercise stringent self-control.

He just had to keep reminding himself that she would never be his. Her heart belonged to another. Whatever he might feel for her, she was not his. He had to be strong and never touch her again, never kiss her again. *Ever*.

Chapter Twelve

❦

Drawing in a deep, steadying breath, Alexander paused outside the breakfast room. He nodded to the footman to indicate that he wasn't yet ready to enter, and spent some time composing himself.

It was time to put his resolve into action—to stay true to the promises he had made to himself last night. His muscles ached slightly, reminding him of his new determination. Arabella van Haven was simply a guest in his home. A guest who would be leaving tomorrow. A guest from whom he would keep his distance. He would not get too close to her, either physically or emotionally. Getting close contained too many dangers. That was all he had to remember.

Forcefully he turned the door handle and strode into the room. The three people sitting at the breakfast table looked up at him and smiled simultaneously: his mother, Charlotte and Miss van Haven.

Seated with her back to the large sash windows, Arabella was bathed in morning sunlight. Alexander almost suspected his mother of placing her where her beauty would be displayed at its most advantageous. The sunlight glinted off the copper strands in her otherwise black hair, her skin appeared luminescent and a golden glow surrounded her—as if she were a maiden in a Renaissance painting.

He nodded a greeting to the three women and turned his back—ostensibly to serve himself from the silver tureens arranged along the sideboard, but in reality to regain his equilibrium and remind himself once again of his resolve. It didn't matter how beautiful she looked in the morning sunlight—not in the slightest. He would not let that or anything else undermine his determination.

Standing straighter, he walked to the table without looking at Arabella, sat down, whipped open his napkin, placed it on his lap and stared down at his food. Why had he served himself a full breakfast when he didn't feel like eating?

He coughed lightly to clear his throat. 'I trust you slept well, Miss van Haven?' he asked, for politeness' sake. From now onwards it would be formality only. She would be Miss van Haven. No more of this calling each other by their first names. After all, look where adopting the more informal American ways had got them. No, he did not wish to go there again.

'I slept very well, thank you, Your Grace.'

Good. She too had the sense to see the necessity of formality. On that it seemed they were in complete agreement.

His mother, however, had raised her eyebrows and was looking from one to the other of them with curiosity. But what his mother thought hardly mattered. It was his mother who had created this problem in the first place, inviting the American heiress into his home without his knowledge or his permission.

'And you, Your Grace? I hope you also slept well.'

Alexander nodded once, quickly, in response to Arabella's enquiry. Yes, he had indeed been able to sleep—but only because he had exercised so furiously he had been in a state of complete physical exhaustion. Without that rigorous swim he doubted he would have been able to chase away thoughts of kissing her, of her soft lips on his, of her pliant body crushed against his, her soft breasts and tight nipples pushing into his chest…

He coughed again as heat flooded his body, then shook his napkin vigorously to drive out those treacherous thoughts and set about carving up his breakfast.

'Well, now that we've established you both slept well, perhaps we can discuss what activities you have planned for the day,' his mother said. 'Alexander, I think it would be a splendid idea if you showed Miss van Haven more of the estate. That is, once you've finished decimating that defenceless kipper.'

Alexander stopped and looked down at the mash of white flesh spread across his plate, then pushed away his uneaten breakfast. 'I'm not sure what Miss van Haven has planned for today, but I intend to inspect the marshlands at the bottom of the estate. The engineers are coming next week, to begin draining the area so it can be turned into viable farmland. I'm sure that would be of no interest to our guest.'

'Oh, I'm sure Miss van Haven would be delighted to accompany you.'

. Alexander inhaled a deep, exasperated breath. Would his mother's infernal meddling never cease? He knew the answer to that. No, of course it would not. Not until Miss van Haven was in her carriage, heading for the railway station and moving out of his life.

'I very much doubt if the marshland would be of any interest to a lady—it's swampy underfoot, and hardly suitable for a leisurely stroll,' he said, hoping that would be the end of the matter.

'Well, if—'

'Nonsense,' his mother answered, cutting off Arabella before she could express her opinion. 'It will give you a chance to show Miss van Haven the parts of the estate she hasn't yet seen—and who knows? She might be interested in your plans for modernisation.'

His mother's lips turned down and her nostrils flared, as if the very idea of anyone being interested in such a subject was extremely unlikely.

'Well, if His Grace would rather—'

'Or you could stay inside all day, Miss van Haven,' his mother interrupted again, a mischievous look sparking in her eyes. 'Our parish priest, the Reverend Truebridge, is an amateur historian, and he has volunteered to give us a talk on the history of Devon—starting with the Bronze Age and working forward to the present day, covering each period in the minutest detail. He can be a little tedious at times, I must admit, and he does tend to go on and on, but he is certainly enthusiastic about his topic. Do you think you might prefer that?'

Arabella's polite smile started to falter, while his mother's smile grew more gleeful.

'After that, some of the older ladies in the party and I are planning on playing cards. Poor Lady Cathridge is having such problems with her lumbago, so we're hoping to discuss that—and many of the other ailments the ladies have suffered with so much over the winter. Aged bodies can be such a trial… The card game will be a good chance for us to catch up and discuss our aches and pains. You're most welcome to join us for that as well, Arabella.'

She smiled with mock innocence at Arabella and waited for her reply. Arabella stared at the Dowager, her brow now deeply furrowed and her lips pinched—like a prisoner watching the iron gates being slammed shut behind her.

Alexander knew he had to offer a reprieve. 'Or if you prefer you can, of course, accompany me. The marshlands may be a bit unsightly, but the walk there will take us through the woodlands and across the farm areas, which are very pleasant at this time of year.'

'Oh, yes, thank you!' she gasped, in obvious gratitude. Recovering, she smiled at his mother. 'And thank *you*, also, Your Grace, for your kind invitation, but I would like to get some fresh air.'

The Dowager smiled in triumph. 'Think nothing of it, my dear. You young people go off and enjoy yourselves.'

'But we must take a chaperon with us.' Alexander stated emphatically.

'Oh, yes—most definitely.'

Arabella's quick response cut Alexander to the quick. She obviously feared being alone with him.

'Nellie will accompany us,' she said.

'That's all settled, then.' His mother smiled. 'And don't feel the need to hurry back—unless, of course, you want to catch some of Reverend Truebridge's talk.'

Alexander glared at his mother. It seemed she had won. Yet again.

Alexander paced backwards and forwards, his boots scrunching on the gravel path, as he waited at the bottom of the stairs for Arabella. A quick walk around the farmlands and back to the house would suffice. That way there would be no danger of them being alone together. They would be in the presence of the tenant farmers through much of the walk, and he was hardly likely to act inappropriately with an audience.

And there would also be Nellie. That should solve both their problems. It would save Arabella from his mother's threat of a torturous death by boredom without the risk of him being alone in her company. Then he could get back to what he'd originally intended for the day: a survey of the marshlands. There was nothing to worry about.

So why did he feel so agitated? He pulled in a few quick breaths to quash the gnawing feeling in the pit of his stomach. This was ridiculous. He did *not* get anxious. And certainly not because of a pretty face.

'Hello, there. I'm ready.'

He turned to see the owner of the pretty face that was causing all this perturbation standing at the top of the stairs, accompanied by her maid. The pretty face was wearing an attractive blue hat that made her crystal-blue eyes even more enchanting.

He coughed to drive away such nonsense. She had a blue hat on which happened to match her eyes. That was all. There was no need to make more of it than that and become absurdly poetical.

'Miss van Haven.' He nodded a terse greeting as she skipped down the stairs.

'Your Grace.' She bobbed a curtsey.

For politeness' sake he offered her his arm, and refused to allow himself to react when he felt the pressure of her gloved hand.

They walked along in silence and Alexander knew that he should make conversation. But what should he say to the woman whom he had taken in his arms and kissed with an intensity as if his very life depended on it? Should he ask about her health? Should he mention how warm it was for this time of year?

No words came, and once again he coughed lightly. This was not like him. He *never* felt awkward. But he was feeling increasingly awkward in her company. Like an adolescent boy unused to the company of the opposite sex. Ridiculous.

'I hope you're not feeling at all worried about what happened last night,' she said, finally breaking the prolonged silence.

About to say he was not worried in the least, he pulled himself up. That would be an outright lie. Of course he was worried by his behaviour. How else should he feel when he had taken advantage of a vulnerable woman for his own lustful purposes?

'I'm very sorry it happened. I can assure you it will never happen again.'

She stopped walking and looked up at him. 'I said last night that you had nothing to be sorry for and I meant it. I would hate what happened to come between us.'

Beseeching eyes stared up at him. Alexander's stern countenance slipped as he stared down at her and he almost forgot his resolve.

He forced himself to look away from those blue eyes and into the distance. 'It is perhaps a bit too late for that.'

'It doesn't have to be, Alexander.' She gripped his arm with both hands, forcing him to look at her. 'You did nothing wrong. I am not offended. The only thing that upsets me is that it has caused a rift between us. I wish we could go back to how we were before the kiss. Then we could be friends again and comfortable in each other's company.'

'But it *did* happen.'

'Well, I can pretend it never happened if you can.'

Was that possible? Alexander doubted he would ever forget what it had been like to take her in his arms, but he nodded his agreement.

'If that is what you wish, Miss van Haven.'

'It is. And I also wish that you would stop being so formal. Call me Arabella again.'

Not for the first time he realised what a re-markable woman she was. She had every right to be offended, to be upset, to be angry, but she was none of those things. Thomas Gardener was most definitely a very lucky man.

He clenched his jaw at the thought of that man—the man who would have what he could not. He dragged in a deep prolonged breath to drive away the ridiculous thought. Jealousy was something else he did not experience, and he wasn't about to start experiencing it now.

'As you wish, Arabella,' he said, through clenched teeth.

Strolling with him arm and arm, Rosie could almost convince herself that things were just the same between her and Alexander. Almost. But she could sense the tension in his body, feel the unease in her own.

While she might not be able to forget that kiss, she knew she had to pretend it had never happened. They had one more day to spend together and she wanted them once again to be relaxed in each other's company. And that wouldn't happen unless they did indeed try and pretend nothing had changed…that they had not experienced that moment of passionate intimacy.

But she most certainly had no intention of trying to forget that kiss. It was the most wonderful thing that had ever happened to her. Yes, it had been wrong—so wrong—but it was something she would always treasure…something she would savour when she was alone.

Kissing him was so completely outside her original plan as to be almost unbelievable. After all, she had arrived with the intention of making the Duke dislike her. She had intended to behave in a manner that would make her a thoroughly unacceptable bride. Instead she had caused this sublimely handsome, imminently eligible man to desire her.

A thrill of excitement ran through Rosie's body. Who would ever have thought it possible that poor little Rosie Smith, an impoverished ward whom nobody ever noticed, would be kissed with such intensity by such a man? But she *had* been.

She ran her tongue along her bottom lip, where his lips had touched, and shivered at the delicious thrill of it all.

'Are you all right, Arabella?' His look was solicitous. 'You're not too cold?'

'Not in the slightest. It's a beautiful day.'

And so it was. The sun was shining in a bright blue sky dotted with puffy white clouds. She was walking through lush green pastures filled with bleating sheep and sweet baby lambs accompanied by a sublimely handsome man. It was indeed a most beautiful day. And her shiver had nothing to do with the temperature, which was delightfully warm.

Rosie gave a contented smile. As long as they remained in public, surely there was no harm in indulging in a little fantasy that she was taking a lovely stroll on the arm of the man who was courting her? It was a fantasy that would come to an end when she left Knightsbrook, and as long as Rosie did nothing to act on it no one would get hurt.

And with Nellie as her chaperon she was safe.

She looked over her shoulder and saw Nellie lagging behind in the distance. It seemed she had already become distracted and oblivious to her duties.

'Do keep up, Nellie!' she called out.

Nellie stopped staring at the farmhands and

rolled her eyes at Rosie in a most un-servant-like manner, but she walked a little faster to catch up.

They resumed their walk, which now took them along the side of a furrowed field, where a line of men and boys were casting seeds from sacks on their backs. As they passed by the men all lifted their cloth caps to Alexander and he shouted out hellos, addressing many by name.

'You seem to know everyone well,' Rosie said, surprised at their informality.

Alexander smiled. 'Yes, I suppose so—but I grew up with them. I almost spent more time with the farmhands as a child than I did with my own family.'

His smile died and he looked out at the tenants, his face solemn.

'Those times were among the happiest of my childhood. My father saw our tenants as a mass of people who worked the land and brought in the revenue that he spent. But I learnt to see each and every one of them as an individual. I could see that they were hard-working people who deserved to be treated with respect.'

He sent her a melancholy smile and she gave his arm a small squeeze.

'Well, it's certainly a beautiful estate to have grown up on. It's so picturesque. Watching the men work is like seeing a painting by Constable come to life,' Rosie said, breathing in the earthy smell of freshly turned soil.

'Yes, my mother would certainly agree with you on that.'

Rosie tilted her head. 'You don't approve?'

'The tenants aren't here to be "picturesque". They want to make a good living—they want the land to be productive. They should be using machinery to plant out the crops and machinery to bring them in. Not doing it by such intense physical labour. If my father had spent as much money updating the estate as he did at the card table these people would not still be involved in such backbreaking toil. And that is something I intend to change.'

Rosie looked at the men labouring over their work and had to agree. She would hate to have to work that hard—especially when there was machinery that could do the work more quickly.

'Oh, yes. You should. If you used steam engines for ploughing the land and bringing in the harvest, it would free up men and you could farm more intensively and diversify your crops.'

He had stopped walking and was now staring down at her, that wonderful smile once again lighting up his face.

'Exactly. That's *exactly* the sort of modern equipment I want to buy. It will transform the estate.'

Rosie smiled back at him. 'If you brought electricity to the estate then the dairy and the shearing sheds could be made much more productive. And if the train came as far as the estate you'd be able to sell produce in London. And once it reaches London, who knows? With refrigeration you could export to Europe and even farther afield. Oh, the possibilities are endless for making this estate really modern and efficient!'

He was still staring down at her, no longer smiling, but looking at her with wide eyes, his eyebrows raised. Rosie suspected she had been babbling.

'I'm sorry. My father was—' She halted as she remembered who she was supposed to be. 'My father has worked with electrical engineers and I think it has instilled in me a love of all technological advances.'

Rosie had only been a young girl of eight when her father had died, but she could still remember the passion in his voice when he'd talked of the progress being made in America, and how electricity was transforming the lives of so many people. Alexander's enthusiasm reminded her of those happy times.

He shook his head and sent her another of those lovely smiles. 'You truly are a remarkable woman, Arabella, and I applaud the fact that you are so enthusiastic about modernisation. Most people of my class are content to continue living as they have for centuries, just sitting back and letting the money roll in from their land. They don't realise that times are changing—that we're being overtaken by the more progressive farming techniques used in America and the Antipodes. But I, for one, am determined not to be left behind. I want to be ready for the twentieth century and all the modern advances it has to offer.'

Arabella smiled, feeling warm inside.

'But unfortunately it will take money—which, thanks to my father, I don't have.'

The tone of his voice had dropped from excitement to pain and anger, and a stab of guilt pierced Rosie's heart. If she hadn't come up with her plan to trick Alexander...if the real Arabella were here instead of her, and if they had actually fallen in love...maybe Arabella's dowry could have been used to settle those debts and modernise the estate. Then the tenants would have had security and Knightsbrook would have been saved.

'So Ara—so my father's money would have gone to good use?' Rosie asked, feeling guilty bile rise up in her throat.

Alexander shook his head. 'It might have been a short-term solution, but it was never something I was prepared to consider. I intend to raise the money through bank loans and make the necessary changes to ensure the estate becomes profitable once more. I want it to be a place where both my family and the tenants feel proud to live. I want the name of Knightsbrook to be an honourable one once again—a name associated with industry, innovation and enterprise. And that won't happen by taking a hand-out from your father.'

Rosie could hear the passion and determination in his voice and she swelled with admiration. He was most definitely a proud man, and she was honoured to be in his company—even if it *was* under false pretences.

The path had reached a stone fence with a wooden stile. Alexander quickly climbed over, then offered his hand to her. She didn't really need his help—she was used to fending for herself— but it was nice to feel his hand in hers once again, even if it was through her linen glove.

She stepped over, and was about to jump down when he placed his hands on her waist and lifted her gently off the wooden step. Her feet touched the ground lightly and his hands remained on her hips, his body close to hers. He stared down into her eyes. She looked up at him expectantly. A gasp escaped her lips and for a hopeful moment she thought he was going to kiss her again.

What she wouldn't give for another kiss…what she wouldn't sacrifice to feel his lips on hers!

His lips drew into a tight line and he removed his hands from her hips. It wasn't to be.

Disappointment, guilt and shame waged a war inside her as they continued their walk in silence, with Nellie trailing along behind. How could she want him to kiss her so much when she knew the harm it would cause? How could she feel so disappointed when she knew they must not kiss? How could she be such a shameful, terrible person?

She cared for Arabella more than she cared for anyone in the world—even more than herself. She would do nothing to hurt her, to tarnish her good name. And yet she still wanted Alexander to take her in his arms, to kiss her. It was beyond reprehensible.

Their walk took them towards a group of thatched cottages nestled together beside a small stream, smoke rising from their chimneys.

'I hope you don't mind,' said Alexander, 'but I can't pass by this way without visiting Annie.'

'Annie?'

Alexander smiled. 'You'll love Annie. She was like a second mother to me and to Charlotte when we were children. More than a second mother.'

A group of women were sitting in a circle outside the cottages, chatting and laughing while they darned socks and mended clothing. When they saw Alexander and Rosie approaching they stopped what they were doing and stood up.

One woman started walking towards them, her arms outstretched. Although her lined, weathered face suggested she was elderly, the woman still had a youthful agility to her movements and a healthy glow on her round cheeks. Her welcoming smile caused Rosie to warm to her immediately, as if she too was being welcomed home by a loving grandmother.

'This is Annie,' Alexander said, his smile growing as wide as the older woman's.

'Alexander!' Annie said, reaching up and embracing him. 'Or should I say Your Grace? I keep forgetting you're all grown-up now. It's so good to see you again.'

'To you, Annie, I will always be Alexander. And it is very good to see *you*—you're looking younger than ever.'

Annie waved her hand at him, as if refusing to take any flattery, but her smile showed how much she enjoyed it. 'And who's this lovely young lady?'

'This is Arabella van Haven—a visitor from America. I'm showing her around the estate.'

'Oh, indeed? So *you're* the young lady from America. Well, well… I'm pleased to meet you, m'lady.'

Annie made a low curtsey, causing Rosie to laugh.

'Please—there's no need for formality with me. I don't have a title.'

Annie's eyebrows rose and she looked sideways at Alexander. 'Not yet, perhaps—but if what the servants up at the big house are saying is right you'll have a title soon enough.'

Rosie waited for Alexander to counter her claim but he merely shrugged, as if to apologise, indicating that even if he didn't agree he wasn't going to contradict Annie.

'So, tell me what's been happening on the estate, Annie?'

'I'll let you know all the gossip—but, please, come inside. I'm sure you'd like tea.'

'Nothing escapes Annie's notice,' Alexander said, still smiling as they followed her inside. 'She knows everyone who works on the estate, and all the people in the village, and everyone knows her.'

Rosie looked around to see where Nellie had got to but she was nowhere in sight. It seemed the call of the library had been too great and she had deliberately hung back once again.

They entered Annie's tidy cottage and were greeted by the welcoming aroma of freshly baked bread. The cottage was simply but pleasantly decorated, with handwoven rugs on the wooden floor, spring flowers in pottery vases and old but comfortable-looking furniture.

Alexander breathed in deeply and smiled. 'That's the smell of my childhood—bread fresh out of the oven.'

They sat down at a scrubbed pine table while Annie put the kettle on the stove and poked some wood into the firebox.

'Charlotte and I spent many hours here at this cottage, gorging ourselves on Annie's cooking and playing in her garden. We probably spent more time here than we did in our own home.'

Rosie could see why any child would want to visit Annie's cottage. It was much more welcoming than the opulence and formality of Knightsbrook House, and there was a caring warmth to Annie that no child would be able to resist.

'Poor Lady Charlotte,' Annie said as she poured hot water into a brown teapot. 'She's such a lovely girl, but so serious. She needs a good man in her life.'

Alexander gave a mock frown. 'Don't let Charlotte hear you say that. She's determined to remain single.'

'Oh, don't worry—I've already told her. She gave me that look she always gives when she hears something she don't like—just like your mam.' Annie pinched her lips together and flared her nostrils, causing Alexander to laugh. 'But I'm very happy *you've* found someone special, Alexander—and such a pretty girl as well.'

Again, Rosie expected Alexander to disabuse Annie, but still he said nothing.

Annie took a golden loaf of bread out of the

oven, and Rosie stood and offered to help. But she was shooed away with a smile and the wave of a tea towel.

'I can already tell she's a good influence on you, Alexander. The last time I saw you, you seemed to be carrying the weight of world on your shoulders and I could barely get a smile out of you.'

She placed the bread on the table, along with the teapot and three teacups. Rosie inhaled the mouth-watering, yeasty aroma. Was there anything more irresistible than freshly baked bread? Rosie doubted it.

'Oh, yes,' Annie continued. 'You need a good woman who'll not only share your burdens but will make you laugh, make you see the joy and wonder in the world. And by look of this pretty young thing she's just the one to do it.'

Annie turned to face Alexander, as if daring him to disagree, but it was a dare that Alexander was apparently reluctant to accept.

When the tea was deemed sufficiently brewed Annie poured. 'You'll be wanting some cheese to go with your bread, won't you, Alexander? Well, you know where it's kept.'

Alexander crossed the small cottage in three steps and took some cheese out of the cupboard while Annie cut doorstop-sized slices of bread.

'As a child I think Alexander lived on my bread

and cheese,' Annie said to Rosie. 'I sometimes wondered whether they ever fed him up at the big house.'

'That's because the cook there could never make bread as good as yours, and there's no better cheese anywhere in the country than the cheese made in your dairy, Annie,' he said as he placed the cheese dish on the table. 'One day soon, when the railway comes through here, I'm hoping that people throughout England will be able to taste the wonderful cheese made in the Knightsbrook dairy under the watchful eye of Annie.'

Annie smiled proudly, cut some generous slices of cheese, and handed plates to Alexander and Rosie.

Rosie took a bite of the still warm bread and murmured her agreement. The cheese had a nutty flavour that was simply delicious. 'I think you're right. This will be very popular. I'm sure it will fetch high prices in London and the other main cities. It's wonderful!'

Alexander took another bite of his own bread and cheese and nodded. He seemed to be enjoying the simple fare much more than the lavish feast that had been served last night in the ornate dining room.

'So, what's been happening on the estate?' Alexander asked again as he served them both another slice of bread and cheese.

Rosie listened as Annie told him all the gossip about the other tenants—about couples who had married, others who were having difficulties, what their children had been up to and who had fallen out with whom.

All the while Annie was talking Rosie watched Alexander. He was smiling, laughing and commiserating about these people he obviously knew well and cared for deeply. The man she was watching was a different man from the one she had first met. He was so much more relaxed sitting in this plain cottage than he was in Knightsbrook House.

Rosie could imagine him as a young boy, running around the fields, playing with the other children on the estate and then, when he was tired and hungry, retreating to Annie's warm, comfortable cottage and the arms of this loving woman.

When she had first met him it would have been impossible for her to imagine that such a commanding man could ever have been a child. He had exuded such authority and been so aloof as he'd glared down at her while she acted the fool.

When Annie finally ran out of gossip Alexander cleared the table, took the plates and cups to the bench and placed the kettle back on the stove to heat up some water for the dishes.

'Oh, be gone with you,' Annie said, flicking a tea towel in his direction. 'I'm not so infirm that

I can't wash a few dishes. You take this young lady on that walk you promised her and leave me to my chores.'

Alexander smiled, then bent down and kissed Annie on the cheek. 'Thank you, Annie. It's been lovely to see you. I'll see you again soon.'

'Mind you do. And tell Charlotte she's due for another visit.'

'I will—I will!'

Annie escorted them to the door and took Rosie's hands in hers. 'I hope to see much more of you too. You'll always be welcome at my cottage.'

Rosie smiled her thank you, even though she knew she would never see this warm, wonderful woman again…

Chapter Thirteen

The world always seemed like a better place after a visit to Annie's cottage. But his conversation with her had also reinforced in Alexander's mind his duty to the tenants. All those people she had talked about depended on Alexander. He had their livelihoods to protect. He needed the estate to survive and prosper as much for their sake as for the sake of his own family.

Annie had said he was like a man with the weight of the world on his shoulders. It wasn't quite the weight of the world he carried, but it was the weight of so many people's futures—futures that his feckless father had put in jeopardy. It was a weight that he had no option but to bear.

Annie had also said that Arabella was the woman who could share his burden, lighten his load and make him laugh. During her short time at Knightsbrook Arabella had most definitely made him laugh. Before her arrival he could hardly remember the last time he had laughed, but in the last two days he had laughed often. She was a woman full of fun, who shared her joy of life with everyone she met. It was a rare and valuable quality that he seemed to be lacking.

He suspected she was also a woman who would gladly share the burdens of the man she loved. Most women of his class expected to live a life of cossetted privilege after they married, in which their burdens were no more exacting than keeping up with the latest fashions and admonishing the servants.

He certainly could not see that in Arabella's future. He imagined that her marriage would be a partnership—that she would ease her husband's burdens, not contribute to them. But whether he was right on that count or not, he was destined never to discover.

Annie had also been right in saying that Arabella was a very pretty young woman. That was something he had been aware of from the moment he had seen her spinning down the entrance hall of Knightsbrook House, and every time he looked at her she seemed to grow more beautiful.

Sitting in Annie's cottage, he had been struck once again by how enchanting she was. It had nothing to do with her fine clothes or her stylish hair; she would be just as beautiful in a simple dress with no adornments. Nor was it her bright blue eyes and creamy skin, fetching though they might be. It was an indefinable inner quality that made her quite radiant.

He smiled at her now and she returned it.

Yes, quite radiant.

They retraced their steps back through the fields. The men all tipped their caps as they passed, and one even called out a greeting to Miss van Haven. Alexander shook his head in disbelief—although he really had no reason to be surprised. Gossip spread faster than wildfire on the estate. No doubt one of the women seated outside Annie's cottage had told the men of their visit, and had informed them about the young woman Alexander was escorting. They had also, no doubt, been told that Arabella was the likely future Duchess of Knightsbrook.

Well, on that, they were going to have to accept disappointment.

Despite her radiant good looks, despite her ready laugh and despite the way she made him feel, she was not for him. She had all the qualities that would make his perfect duchess, but it was not going to happen.

Annie had said he needed a woman who would lighten his burdens, but his burdens seemed even heavier now that he had met Arabella. Yes, it had been a long time since he had laughed—and he suspected that when Arabella left, when she returned to Thomas Gardener, she would take the laughter with her.

They walked on along the tree-lined path down to the river, then halted together to take in the tranquil scene. This had always been his favourite spot on the estate when he was a child, and it looked particularly beautiful at this time of year. Weeping willows bearing their bright green spring foliage dipped in the gently running water, and multi-coloured wildflowers dotted the long grass.

'It's lovely—and so peaceful,' she murmured

It was indeed. All they could hear was the gentle babbling of the river running over mossy rocks and the sound of birds chirping in the foliage.

He led her along the edge of the river until they reached a stone seat beside the old, now abandoned mill.

'I spent hours here as a child,' Alexander said almost to himself as he took a seat beside Arabella. 'It was a place to play but also my sanctuary—somewhere to escape from "the big house", as Annie insists on calling it.'

'A place for a child to get dirty and have adventures?' she said with a laugh.

'Indeed.'

'I can just imagine you as a small boy, your knees muddy, trying to catch fish and skimming stones across the river.'

Alexander smiled as memories came back to him. When he'd got away from the house and played on the estate with the tenants' children his childhood days had been almost carefree.

'My record was eight bounces.'

She gave a little laugh. 'Really? Prove it.'

Alexander turned to face her. 'What? You don't believe me?'

Smiling, she shook her head.

'Well, then…' Alexander stood, took off his jacket, rolled up his shirtsleeves and looked around for a suitable stone. 'It's been a long time, and I'm somewhat out of practice…'

'Oh, excuses, excuses.'

To his surprise she stood up, picked up her own stone and stood beside him.

'I challenge you to a duel!' she said.

'You're on.'

Side by side, they bent their knees, leant back and flicked their stones across the river's surface. Alexander had no idea how many times his own stone skipped because he was watching Arabella's stone fly across the river, bouncing once, twice, three times.

'Well done!' he exclaimed in amazement. It was obviously not the first time she had skimmed stones.

'But not good enough. You beat me by one.'

'Well, I do have the home advantage.'

She let out a delightful tinkling laugh. 'Ever the gentleman. So, are you ready for a rematch? Then I'll be able to find out if you're as much of a gentleman in defeat as you are in victory.'

'I accept your challenge,' he said, and immediately began searching for appropriate stones.

Caught up in the game, he lost count of the number of stones they threw, or who was winning—he just knew it was a long time since he'd enjoyed such childlike pleasure

Having skimmed all the flat stones they could find, they collapsed, laughing, onto the stone bench.

'I think we should declare it a draw,' Alexander said.

Arabella nodded her agreement. 'That was fun. Do you come down here often?'

'This is where I first met Annie. Charlotte and I had escaped from the house because Father was hosting another one of his week-long gambling parties and Mother had taken to her rooms, supposedly with one of her headaches. Charlotte was crying and I was trying to comfort her. Annie found us, took us back to her cottage, fed us and let us stay the night. After that, every time there was a house party the two of us would immediately escape and spend time at Annie's. She saved us from what would have been a miserable childhood.'

'She's a lovely woman,' said Arabella quietly. 'You were lucky to have someone so warm to comfort you as a child.'

Alexander nodded. 'But I haven't been back here for years. Not since…'

He paused and began thinking back to when he had last sat here by the river. He certainly hadn't been since his father had died and he had taken control of the near-bankrupt estate. The moment the lawyers had informed him of the state of the accounts had heralded the end of all frivolity. It must have been some time before that. Whenever it had been, it was a considerable time ago, but exactly when he could not recall.

'Not since Lydia?'

Her voice was quiet but her words hit him like a cannon ball, knocking the wind out of his lungs.

'I'm sorry, Alexander.' She placed her hand gently on his arm. 'I shouldn't have mentioned her name—not if it pains you.'

Alexander shook his head. 'No, it doesn't pain me.' And he realised that it was true. Not so long ago his grief over Lydia had been so intense he'd preferred to try and forget she had ever existed, had ever been part of his life. Now he had no objection to talking about her.

'Lydia was the love of my life. She was the woman I intended to marry.'

Arabella nodded but said nothing.

'She was a cheerful and loving young woman.' Alexander sighed, remembering what Lydia had been like when they were young. 'But she changed. And that, too, was my father's fault. He ran regular card evenings at the house. They were not sociable events, like the ones my mother hosts, where gossip is more important than winning or losing. These were serious gambling events, where fortunes could easily be lost. And reputations.'

He stopped talking for a moment and looked out into the distance.

'Usually I was able to protect Lydia from the excesses of those weekends, but she visited one weekend when I was away and met one of my father's gambling companions…'

He paused again, and considered how much he should reveal about that debauched man to a woman as innocent as Arabella. He was a notorious rake—a man who loved corrupting innocent young women. And that was exactly what he had done to Lydia.

'She thought she was in love with him and that he was in love with her. She fell in with his lifestyle—the parties, the gambling… Gambling and that man became all she lived for. Then she started to lose. A lot. That was when the real change happened. She borrowed money. She lied to everyone she knew—including me—to get more. She even started to steal from people to pay her gambling debts. I tried to help her...to encourage her to stop... But nothing I did worked. *Nothing*.'

They sat in silence for a moment, both staring into the gently burbling river.

'Where is she now?' Arabella asked, her voice almost a whisper.

'Her debts grew so big she eventually fled to the Continent. I believe the wastrel left her and moved on to his next conquest. The last I heard she was working as a—'

But Arabella did not need to know the extent of Lydia's downfall. She didn't need to know that Lydia had attached herself to a series of wealthy but increasingly disreputable men in order to support her gambling habit, until she'd been reduced to selling herself in order to fund her desperate lifestyle.

'The last I heard she was working at a gambling establishment in Italy.'

An establishment where the women dealt more than just cards.

'It must have been painful for you,' said Arabella.

Alexander nodded. 'It was very painful to watch someone I cared about change and be powerless to do anything about it. It was painful to hear her constant lies. Eventually it was as if every word that came out of her mouth was a lie. She lied about the extent of her debts. She lied about how much money she had lost. And she lied about how she had managed to repay those debts.' Alexander shook his head. 'I sometimes wonder if she was so lost that she no longer knew when she was telling the truth and when she was lying.'

He sighed deeply. It was the first time he had told anyone about Lydia's downfall. It had always been too painful to remember it before, and certainly too painful to talk about it. At the time he had done everything he could to help her. Tried endless ways to keep her away from that man, from the card table and the gaming houses, and in the process of trying to save Lydia he had lost part of himself. He had lost his trust in people, and lost his ability to relax and enjoy himself.

He shook his head, picked up another stone and tossed it into the river. The reality was that there was nothing more he could have done for Lydia. For years he had tortured himself with guilt. Had believed that if only he had been at home that weekend Lydia might never have met that terrible man. Had thought that perhaps there were things he could have done to turn her away from her downward spiral.

But Lydia's path was one she had chosen for herself. Continuing to torture himself about what he might have done, what he might have said to stop her would help no one—not him, and not Lydia.

He sighed again, then smiled at Arabella. 'In answer to your question, I don't remember the last time I visited this spot on the river, but I'm pleased I brought you here today.'

She smiled sadly and nodded. 'So am I.'

It seemed Annie was right again: talking to Arabella had lifted the weight of the guilt and remorse over Lydia that he had been carrying for many years, and he felt much lighter for it.

Thomas Gardener was a lucky man to have a woman like Arabella in his life. She was indeed a woman who could lighten a man's burdens and take away his worries. He could only hope the man appreciated what a treasure he had. A woman who was not only beautiful, but also clever, funny and supportive.

But this would not do. He had originally decided to take a quick stroll around the estate to save Arabella from the ordeal of a dreary talk by the Reverend Truebridge and the horror of playing cards with his mother and her cronies. Instead he had lost all sense of time.

He looked up at the sky. The sun was heading towards the horizon and there was a slight chill in the air. It must be late-afternoon. He picked up his jacket and pulled his fob watch out of the pocket. Yes, he was right. Time had got away from them, and instead of a quick stroll they had been away all day. It seemed that in Arabella's company he even forgot the passage of time.

His mother would certainly be pleased, and would no doubt read much more into their absence than it warranted.

He stood up, took her hand and helped her to her feet. It had been a delightful day but it was time to bring it to an end.

'I suspect my mother and her friends will have finished their card game, and that every ache and pain will have been discussed in exhaustive detail, so it should be safe to return to the house.'

She gave a light laugh and rolled her eyes. 'Oh, yes—I haven't thanked you for saving me from that ordeal, have I? It's been a lovely day, Alexander.'

He draped his jacket over one shoulder, dangling it from his thumb, and took Arabella's arm in his. Slowly they walked back along the river, as if neither was in any hurry to return to the house. White swans sailed majestically past them, ducks dived in the water and birds flitted between the trees, fully occupied with finding food for their offspring and oblivious to the couple walking in companionable silence beneath them.

For the first time in many years Alexander enjoyed the simple pleasure that nature brought and the soothing effect it could have on the soul.

They followed the path from the river and walked under the canopy of the tree-lined path that led back to the house. A light, rustling breeze shook the trees, and Arabella lifted her hands and laughed as a cascade of spring blossoms showered them, falling like pink confetti.

She took hold of her skirts and gave them a shake, sending tiny flowers skittering in all directions, while Alexander brushed the blossoms off his shoulders.

'Leave them,' she said, laughing. 'Pink really suits you.'

'I'm not sure about that, but the blossoms adorning your hair are certainly fetching.' He laughed too, and picked a few of the flowers off her hat.

Leaning over her, he could feel the warmth of her body, could almost feel her soft curves, almost taste her silky skin. He closed his eyes and breathed in deeply, inhaling the remembered scent of fresh flowers.

This could not be happening. He had to resist temptation. He could not take her in his arms again. He could not kiss her again. Even if her feminine scent was overwhelming his senses… even if every inch of his body longed to take her in his arms. Even if his throbbing desire was telling him how much he wanted her. This could not happen.

He had to remember his vow. He had to remember his aching muscles, remember his plunge into cold water, how hard he'd had to exercise last night to try and free himself from his desire for her.

Opening his eyes, he discovered his hand was suspended in mid-air above her head, clasping a pink blossom. Despite his self-admonition on the dangers of touching her, he ran his hand down her soft cheek.

Her breath caught in her throat as she stared up at him, her pink lips parted tantalisingly. Even while words of warning rang in his head, he took hold of her chin, tilted it towards him and leant in closer.

How could he not kiss her again? How could he deny himself such temptation? How could he not do what his body was commanding him to do?

But his mind knew better than his body. She was not his. She would never be his.

He released her chin, stood up straight and looked off into the distance.

'We can't do this.' He heard the formality in his voice, so at odds with how he was feeling. 'Don't you agree?'

He looked down and saw her blink a few times, as if unsure she had heard him correctly.

'Don't you agree?' he repeated. Surely she,

even more than he, could see the folly of their actions.

'I agree,' she said, in a barely audible whisper.

Once again they walked in silence, although now that sense of companionship had evaporated, to be replaced with a tense uneasiness.

Alexander knew he deserved to feel uncomfortable. He had allowed his desires to overcome his good sense. Wasn't that exactly why he had wanted to avoid being alone with Arabella? And hadn't he been proved correct?

They entered the house and he bowed to her formally, as if their encounter had never happened…as if he hadn't almost kissed her…as if he hadn't unburdened his soul and shared with her intimate details of his relationship with Lydia.

'It is nearly time to change for dinner. I'll bid you farewell till then.'

He bowed again, and then, like the coward he knew himself to be, retreated to his rooms.

Chapter Fourteen

'Ooh, lovely—a bath. Thank you, Nellie, that's exactly what I need.'

Rosie stripped off her dress and undergarments and lowered herself into the warm water of the freshly drawn bath. She slid down until only her head was above the water and rested her head on the soft towel Nellie had kindly draped on the edge of the bath for that purpose. Perhaps Nellie was feeling guilty for abandoning her duties as chaperon, but this bath more than made up for it.

A small fire flickered in the tiled fireplace of the chamber adjoining her bedroom, making the room warm and cosy, and Rosie issued a small sigh of complete contentment.

This was perfection itself. A chance to lie back and have a long, leisurely soak. She picked up the soft sponge and the rose-scented soap, worked up a lather and gently ran the sponge over her body while her mind wandered to the day's events.

And what a day it had been.

It was possibly the happiest day she had ever experienced, and even Alexander's formal parting could not detract from her joy. A few days ago Rosie would not have thought it possible that she could spend such a wonderful day with a man as charming as Alexander Fitzroy, Duke of Knightsbrook.

After her treatment by every man who had ever entered the van Haven home, being snubbed was all Rosie had known. It was a role she had accepted—the poor ward who had no prospects and was of no interest to any man. But not any more.

A man who was head and shoulders above all those men—literally and figuratively—had spent the day with her, had laughed with her, played games with her, unburdened his troubles to her. He had treated her as an equal—more than an equal—and as someone whose views he respected and admired. And, what was more, he had almost kissed her. *Again.*

Rosie wiggled her toes above the warm water and closed her eyes as images of everything that had happened ran past her mind's eye—from Alexander's stiff greeting in the breakfast room through to their enjoyable lunch at Annie's, from their playful encounter by the river to his revelations about Lydia, and then to that almost-kiss under the blossoms.

She squeezed the sponge and released a stream of scented soap bubbles into the water. Oh, yes. It had been quite a day. Within the space of a few hours she had seen so many sides to Alexander. The stern man at the breakfast table. The loving man in Annie's cottage. The childlike man who had skimmed stones on the river. The serious, almost melancholy man who had talked of Lydia. And the passionate man whose hungry eyes had burned into hers when he had nearly kissed her again.

So many men—and she adored them all. Even the stern Alexander. She knew where *that* man came from. As Annie had said, he carried the weight of the world on his shoulders—the responsibility for his family, for his tenants, and his need to undo the damage his father had done to the family name.

And he also carried the weight of wanting to do the right thing when he was with her. She was sure it was only the non-existent Thomas Gardener that had stopped him from taking her in his arms this afternoon and kissing her.

Rosie squeezed the sponge again and let soapy water run over her shoulders and down her chest as she contemplated how she could get rid of pesky Thomas Gardener. Perhaps she could tell Alexander that she had just had news that the unfortunate man had suddenly dropped dead, or had decided to become a monk instead of marrying her, or had set off for an expedition to deepest Africa and was unlikely to be seen again.

She sighed and rubbed the sponge slowly across her shoulder and down her arm. None of those stories had the slightest chance of being believed. It seemed the imaginary Thomas Gardener was going to have to stay healthy, alive and working at his family's bank for a few days more.

And at least he did serve one valuable purpose. If Thomas Gardener hadn't stopped Alexander from kissing her, Rosie doubted if anything else would have—certainly not her. She sighed again. She was a terrible friend. She knew she had to protect Arabella's reputation, and yet she seemed to forget all about that whenever there was a chance that Alexander might kiss her.

It was as if she was powerless to stop the way she felt about him.

Rosie stopped rubbing her arm and dropped the sponge, then sat up straighter in the bath and gasped.

The way she felt about him?

It was obvious how she felt about him. She had fallen in love with him.

Her hand covered her mouth, as if she must stop herself from blurting out this shocking revelation. But it was true. She had to face the facts.

She had fallen in love with Alexander, Lord Ashton, the Eighth Duke of Knightsbrook.

She lowered her hand, picked up the floating sponge and clasped it to her chest. This had most certainly not been part of the plan she had devised over tea and scones at The Ritz just a few days ago. No, falling in love had been the last thing on her mind. Less than the last thing. It had been so unlikely that she had never even considered it.

But that was before she had met Alexander. She sighed loudly and shook her head. How could she *not* fall in love with a man like Alexander?

'There's an awful lot of sighing going on in there,' Nellie said, poking her head around the corner, a clothes brush in her hand. 'Are you all right? Is the water too hot? Too cold?'

'No, it's perfect.'

'So what's all this sighing about?'

'It's just been rather a confusing day, that's all.'

'Don't worry,' Nellie said, heading back into the bedroom. 'Only one more evening and we'll be back in London. This will all be over.'

Rosie couldn't stop herself from sighing once again. This time in frustration. One more evening. That was all. After that she would never see Alexander again. She would have to live without him in her life.

How was she going to be able to bear that?

And it was obvious that Alexander felt something for her as well. That look on his face when he had almost kissed her... He felt it too. Could it be that the Eighth Duke of Knightsbrook *would* consider marrying someone like plain Rosie Smith?

She squeezed hard on the sponge. Oh, what would it be like to be married to Alexander? Bliss. That was what it would be. Pure bliss.

She sighed again and sank down into the water.

But he didn't even know Rosie Smith.

She shot back up.

He thought she was Arabella van Haven. How would he react when he realised she wasn't the daughter of a wealthy banker but an orphan without a penny to her name?

She dragged herself out of the bath and wrapped herself in the soft white towel. Alexander wasn't a snob. He didn't want Arabella's money. Didn't want to marry an heiress. Wasn't it possible he *might* want to marry her, the real Rosie Smith, a woman with no money? Was she being unrealistic to think that he would consider someone of her background as a potential bride? Was that just too ridiculous?

Well, there was only one way to find out.

Rosie padded on bare feet through to her bedroom, where Nellie had laid out her undergarments and the pale blue gown she was to wear that evening.

She would just have to tell him who she really was and see how he reacted. Only then would she know how he felt about the real her, Rosie Smith. That was exactly what she would do.

She sat down at her dressing table, nodded at her reflection, then frowned. But she would have to tell Arabella first. After all, Arabella had agreed to a plan in which Rosie behaved so abominably that the Duke would not *want* to marry her. She had not agreed to a plan in which Rosie pretended to be Arabella and then, when it suited her, let the cat out of the bag and announced to everyone that she wasn't Arabella after all.

No, she owed it to Arabella to let her know first. And then she would tell Alexander.

Yes, that was a much better plan. It was all settled.

With a light step she skipped down the stairs and entered the dining room, to find the family already seated.

Alexander stood up and a footman ushered her to her seat.

'What happened to the other guests?' Rosie asked as she took her seat.

The footman shook out her napkin with a practised flourish and placed it on her lap, and Rosie smiled her thanks.

'The other guests were invited only for yesterday evening so they could meet you,' the Dowager said, signalling to the footman to begin serving the soup. 'Tonight it's family only.'

'Family and one guest,' Alexander added.

It seemed formal Alexander was back again. Rosie smiled at him. She loved even formal Alexander, the honourable man who was so determined to do the right thing.

'Quite right, Alexander.' The Dowager raised her wine glass. 'To our honoured guest, Arabella van Haven, who already feels like part of the family.'

Alexander glared at his mother and received an equally reproving glare in return, before she turned her attention back to Rosie. 'So, Miss van Haven, did Alexander show you the rest of the estate. It's magnificent, isn't it?'

'Oh, yes. We met some of the tenants and had a lovely walk along the river. It really is quite beautiful.'

The Dowager smiled her approval. 'Indeed it is. And it's so lovely to see the tenants working on the land in the same way they have for generations. So much nicer than horrid steam engines. Steam is diabolical, don't you think?'

Rosie bit her lip to stop her smile as Alexander continued to glare at his mother. 'Well, a "diabolical" steam train brought me here from London. And an even more diabolical steam ship meant I could cross the Atlantic in seven days in considerably more comfort than I would have had I travelled by sailing ship. So, if it weren't for steam I doubt I'd be here this evening.'

'Well, there's that, I suppose…' the Dowager conceded reluctantly. 'But there should be limits to all this modernisation.'

Alexander shook his head and exhaled loudly.

'Did you have a chance to meet Annie?' Charlotte asked, interrupting what Rosie suspected was a familiar argument between the Dowager and Alexander.

'Oh, yes—she made us tea and served us some freshly baked bread and the most delicious cheese I've ever tasted.'

Charlotte smiled and nodded. 'I must go down and visit her tomorrow. Perhaps we could go together in the morning? It would be lovely if we had a chance to spend some time together before you return to London.'

Rosie smiled at the young woman, touched by her offer of friendship. 'I'd enjoy that very much.'

Polite conversation continued throughout all the courses, with just the occasional black look from Alexander when his mother alluded to the topic of marriage or the horrors of the modern world.

'I hear you're an accomplished banjo player, Miss van Haven,' the Dowager said when the meal was almost over. 'Perhaps you can entertain us after dinner? I bought a banjo especially for this weekend.'

Rosie almost choked on her chocolate mousse, and took a sip of water while she recovered herself. 'I suspect my abilities on the banjo have been greatly exaggerated. Unless you enjoy the sound of cats being strangled it might be best to keep me away from that particular instrument.'

The Dowager's lips pinched slightly. 'Then perhaps you would care to recite some verses for us from Shakespeare?'

Oh, dear. She had helped Arabella learn her lines for various Shakespeare plays, but unfortunately had retained none of them.

'I'm afraid in that area too my talents may have been exaggerated.'

The Dowager's already pinched lips tightened further. 'What *are* your accomplishments, my dear?'

'Well, I have some talent on the piano, and I have taken singing lessons.'

'Wonderful.' The pinched lips turned into a smile. 'The piano is so much more cultivated than the banjo, anyway. After dinner you can play for us.'

'I'd be delighted.'

Rosie smiled. There were so many accomplishments Mr van Haven could have attributed to his daughter—but the *banjo*? What had he been thinking? Well, he hadn't been thinking… It seemed he rarely thought of his daughter and didn't know anything about her.

Their meal finished, they rose from the table and all followed the Dowager into her private drawing room, where a grand piano took pride of place.

Rosie sat at the piano and shuffled through the sheets of music until she found one of her favourite pieces, while the family seated themselves and turned towards her with expectant faces.

The piano had been a means of escape for her ever since she was a little girl, and she soon lost herself in the music, forgetting about her game-playing, forgetting about the way she was deceiving the friend she loved, even for a moment forgetting about Alexander.

When she came to the end of Beethoven's 'Moonlight Sonata' she turned to face the family. The room remained silent. Had she done something wrong?

Then Charlotte, the Dowager and Alexander stood as one and applauded enthusiastically.

'It seems you have been hiding the truth,' Alexander said as he continued to clap his hands.

Heat rushed to Rosie's cheeks. He had finally found her out. But how? And which of the many lies she had told was he referring to?

'You have more than *"some talent"*. You're a virtuoso,' he continued. 'I don't think I've ever heard that piece played with more beauty and more warmth.'

Her cheeks grew hotter—but from pleasure, not discomfort. 'Thank you,' she murmured, and turned back to the piano.

His praise had touched her deeply. It seemed there was another Alexander she was also in love with. The one who looked at her with tender admiration.

Chapter Fifteen

She was continually amazing him. Beautiful, funny—and now it seemed she was also talented. He watched her shuffle through the music sheets, looking for another piece to play, her pretty forehead furrowed in concentration.

She was not the way his mother had described her when she had first been trying to convince him that he should marry an American heiress. And it seemed her claim that she played the banjo was wrong—thank goodness. But his mother was right in that the man she married would be very lucky indeed.

It was just a shame it wouldn't be him.

If it wasn't for Thomas Gardener he would have no reservations about courting her, despite her father's fortune.

Yes, he'd always had objections to marrying anyone—and an American heiress in particular—but whether that was due to pride, his worry that people would assume he had married for money, or because Lydia had put him off love and marriage for ever, he couldn't say. Whatever it was, all those reasons were losing their hold.

When it came to her father's fortune there would be options. An astute businessman like Mr van Haven would surely prefer to invest his money in the estate and be paid a healthy return rather than merely hand over money in the form of a dowry. And if people thought he had married Arabella for her father's money, so what? He couldn't possibly be so shallow that he would let what others thought of him dictate his actions.

He did care about restoring the nobility and prestige of the family name, but that was in order to honour his ancestors' hard work and the sacrifices they had made. And a respected name was something he wished to pass on to future generations of FitzRoys. It wasn't because he cared what others thought of him personally.

And as for the pain that Lydia had caused him—well, that was fading into a distant memory. It was no longer an obstacle when it came to thoughts of marriage. And Arabella was nothing like Lydia, with all her lies and complications.

But all that was neither here nor there. Arabella was in love with Thomas Gardener. She wanted to marry Thomas Gardener—not him.

He was sick to death of Thomas Gardener.

Arabella replaced the sheets of music on the piano stand, turned around on the piano bench and smiled. 'If you'll indulge me, I think I'll play a tune that I've learnt just recently. When I was in New York I bought a book of contemporary English songs and fell in love with them. I'm playing from memory, so please excuse any mistakes.'

'Oh, I'm sure it will be wonderful,' his mother said, beaming with pleasure. 'Play on…play on.'

Arabella gave a cheeky grin and began playing the opening bars of the music hall song 'Champagne Charlie'. Alexander suppressed a smile as he watched his mother to see how she would react to such a low-class form of entertainment being performed in her private drawing room?

When Arabella sang the first few lines in a false Cockney accent his mother's smile quivered, but then it returned even wider and she started clapping along to the tune.

Unbelievable. Arabella had got the wife of the Seventh Duke of Knightsbrook clapping along to a music hall song. Simply amazing.

When she repeated the chorus—*Champagne Charlie is me name, Champagne drinking is me game*—the Dowager and Charlotte even joined in, leaving Alexander so stunned his mouth literally fell open.

'Oh, that was so funny!' his mother said when Arabella had finished, wiping away a tear.

'*"Champagne Charlie is me name..."* Oh, yes, very funny.'

Arabella smiled. 'What would you like next? More Beethoven or more music hall?'

'Music hall! Music hall,' his mother and Charlotte chanted together.

Alexander shook his head in surprise and admiration. Anyone who could get Charlotte to laugh so easily and his mother and sister to enjoy each other's company really was special. He was beginning to wonder whether he should let Thomas Gardener have things all his own way.

After all, wasn't all fair in love and war? And he was most certainly falling in love with Arabella van Haven...

She began a round of music hall songs, many of which Alexander had heard before, and he noticed she skipped the bawdier verses. A wise decision. It was surprising enough to see his mother enjoying something she would normally dismiss as common; if she knew the true lyrics Alexander suspected it would be a step too far.

Arabella finished and turned to her appreciative audience.

Clapping enthusiastically, his mother stood up and approached the piano. 'That was marvellous, Arabella. Just marvellous. Thank you so much. I can't remember the last time I enjoyed myself this much. But I'm getting tired, so I think I'll retire.' She gave Charlotte a pointed look. 'And I believe *you* were hoping to get an early night as well—weren't you, Charlotte?'

'No.' Charlotte shook her head, then noticed her mother angling her head in Alexander's direction. 'Oh, yes... I was.' Charlotte gave a fake yawn. 'I'm rather tired also, so I think I'll retire early as well.'

Charlotte joined her mother at the piano and kissed Arabella's cheek. 'Thank you so much. For once Mother and I are in total agreement. That was the most fun this family has had for a long time.'

'Yes, yes, it was wonderful,' his mother said, leaning over to kiss Arabella's cheek, and jutting out her elbow in the strangest manner as she did so. Her arm caught the edge of the pile of sheet music and sent the pages scattering to the floor. 'Oh, dear, I beg your pardon. Alexander, help Arabella pick up that music—and come on, Charlotte. It's time we retired.'

She grabbed Charlotte's arm and hurried her out of the room. When the door had closed he could hear the two women giggling and humming the last tune as they headed up the stairs.

Alexander shook his head, still looking at the door. It was an unsubtle move on his mother's part to leave them alone together, but then subtlety had never been his mother's strong suit.

He turned to face Arabella. The room suddenly seemed very quiet. He remained standing in the middle of the room, staring down at Arabella, feeling uncharacteristically awkward. Then he bent down and picked up the scattered sheets and handed them to her.

She shuffled them into an orderly pile, placed them on the music stand, then picked them up again and gripped them in tight hands. It seemed she too was nervous now that they were alone.

And perhaps she was right to be nervous. If she knew what he was about to do…

He sat down beside her on the piano bench and heard the breath catch in her throat. Had he deliberately sat so close that his leg was touching hers? Perhaps. Or had he wanted to be close so he could surround himself in that beautiful floral scent? Whatever it was, being so close to her was intoxicating his senses and making him forget what he wanted to say.

'Thank you for that, Arabella,' he said finally. 'Charlotte was right. That was the most fun our family has had in a long time. You have certainly brought laughter into this house. And I've never seen Charlotte and my mother leave a room together singing. I would never have thought such a thing possible. You really are a remarkable woman.'

'Oh, I'm pleased they enjoyed it.'

She shuffled the music sheets again, put them on the stand, then picked them up once more.

'You really *are* a remarkable woman, Arabella,' he repeated.

She sent him a small smile. 'Well, I love to play the piano and I enjoy singing.'

'It's more than that.' He took the sheets of music from her hands, placed them on the music stand, then took her hands in his.

She looked down at her small hands, encased in his larger ones, then back up at him, her blue eyes sparkling in the candlelight.

'You are truly exceptional, Arabella. You're funny, clever, kind, sweet…and now it seems you're talented as well. You're the most wonderful woman I have ever met.'

'Oh!' she gasped.

'And, what's more, I think I've fallen in love with you.'

Her eyes momentarily grew larger, then she blinked rapidly. 'You think you've…?' She closed her eyes, as if trying to absorb this surprising admission.

'No, I'm wrong. I don't *think* I've fallen in love with you.'

Her eyes sprang open.

'I *know* I've fallen in love with you.' He smiled, feeling buoyant, as if his declaration had cut loose the weights that were tying him down. 'Nothing would give me more pleasure than to court you, one day to marry you.'

'But I…' She swallowed, her breath coming in gasps. 'I…um…'

'I know. I know,' he interrupted, desperate to put her at her ease. 'I've put you in an impossible position. You're already in love with another man—all but betrothed to Thomas Gardener. But I could not let you leave this house without telling you how I feel.'

Her blinking became more rapid. 'Oh, Thomas Gardener… Yes. Him.' She chewed lightly on her lower lip.

Not for the first time Alexander cursed the man's existence, and ungraciously wished that some accident might befall him and take him out of Arabella's life. Or, better still, that Arabella would decide she no longer loved him, making the path easier for Alexander.

But what was the chance of that happening?

Alexander had to know whether he was chasing an impossible dream.

'And I could not let you leave without finding out how you felt about me. I know you said you were in love with him, but do I stand any chance of winning your affections?'

Alexander held his breath and waited for her answer. She was looking down at their hands. He followed her gaze and saw her small hands were clenched into fists inside his larger ones.

She hadn't spoken, but that gesture had given him an answer. It was not one he wanted, but it was one he would abide by.

'Forgive me, Arabella.' He released her hands. 'I've spoken out of turn. I've embarrassed you and made you feel uncomfortable.'

'No, no—not at all.' She took hold of one of his hands in both of hers, clasping it tightly. 'It's just complicated. I need to return to London. There are people I need to talk to before I can tell you how I feel. All I can say is that you have done nothing for which you need to beg my forgiveness. You have not embarrassed me nor made me feel uncomfortable. Quite the contrary.'

He brushed a stray curl back from her face. 'Thank you, Arabella. Thank you for giving me hope,' he murmured.

She angled her head as he ran his hand along her soft cheek. Closing her eyes, she parted her lips slightly, her breath turning to a quick gasp.

His gaze lingered on those soft lips, parted so invitingly. She had given him hope—hope that she would one day be his. Surely that was enough? But those lips…those beautiful, full pink lips…how could he resist?

Perhaps just one small kiss?

He leant forward, unable to fight the fierce

urge building up inside him. His lips lightly touched hers. A sound escaped her mouth. Was it a gasp or a moan? Whatever it was, it caused her lips to part further, and they remained parted, seemingly asking him to intensify the kiss.

If that was what she was asking, then it was a request he was more than happy to grant.

He pulled her into his arms and kissed her harder, more deeply. Her sigh of pleasure as he used his tongue to open her mouth told him he had not misread her actions. And when her hands encircled his neck he had definitive proof.

She wanted this as much as he did. And he most certainly wanted this kiss—desperately wanted it, and much more.

A powerful need was driving him on, and he licked those sweet lips, desperate to devour her feminine taste, to devour *her*. Her need matched his own, and she ran her hands through his hair, clasping him close, seemingly urging him on. Then, to his immense pleasure, her tongue entered his mouth, tasting, probing, teasing.

She was just as lost as he was. He would make her forget Thomas Gardener…make her surrender herself to the pleasure he was giving her…make her think only of him.

He clasped her slim waist and pulled her in, closer towards him, impatient to feel those soft breasts against his chest. Even through the silk of her gown her nipples pushed hard, and he could feel the fast beating of her heart.

Her arousal was driving him almost insane with desire, and he kissed her neck, savouring the taste of her soft, warm skin. He heard her purr with pleasure as his lips trailed a line across the naked skin of her chest and along the soft mounds of her breasts, which were rising and falling with each rapid breath.

His hunger for her was rising to an almost insatiable level, and he was tempted to tear open the delicate fabric of her gown, to feast himself on her beautiful body. But he would not compromise the woman he loved.

He withdrew from her and bit down hard on his lip, hoping the pain would distract his mind and his body. He would do nothing to harm her or compromise her. Instead he would lovingly recall every erotic detail of their encounter when he was alone in his room—the touch and taste of her skin, her intoxicating feminine scent, and that look of sensual abandonment on her face.

She remained in his arms, her eyes closed, her lips parted, her face flushed. His erection was almost unbearable now, but that was a price he had to pay.

'So, can I take it from your reaction that I have a chance against Thomas Gardener?'

She slowly opened her eyes and blinked a few

times. 'Oh, you most certainly do,' she said, her voice husky. 'After a kiss like that I'm beginning to think that Thomas Gardener is just a figment of my imagination. It's as if he doesn't exist at all.'

That was exactly the response Alexander wanted.

With final victory now close at hand, he took her in his arms and kissed her again.

Chapter Sixteen

Was there ever a more wonderful day? Rosie stretched luxuriously in the four-poster bed. It was as if her entire body was smiling with contentment. Today she would return to London. She would recount to Arabella every delightful, delicious detail of what had happened over the weekend. Then, with Arabella's blessing, she would pen a letter to Alexander and confess all.

In her letter she would tell him that she loved him, loved everything about him, and most of all loved the way he made her feel. All would be revealed—who she really was, what her silly scheme had been about, and the reasons why she had been pretending to be Arabella—and then everything would be put to rights.

She stretched again, her smile turning into a sigh of pure pleasure. It was a perfect plan and one she could hardly wait to put into action. It certainly wasn't her original plan, but this new plan was so much better.

Everything had turned out perfectly. Arabella was saved from an unwanted marriage and could now pursue her real love—the theatre. And Rosie had met a man who had swept her off her feet and changed her life for ever. She had received a declaration of love and had been given a delightful taste of what it would be like to be loved by a man like Alexander FitzRoy. It was all perfect.

Sweeping back the covers just as Nellie arrived to help her dress for the morning, Rosie all but danced across the room, threw open the curtains and looked out at the grey cloudy sky, edged with threatening black rain clouds lining the horizon.

'Have you ever seen a more beautiful day, Nellie?' She beamed a smile at Arabella's lady's maid.

'Well, *you're* certainly in a good mood,' Nellie said, giving her a sideways glance.

Rosie did a twirl in front of Nellie. 'Indeed I am. Oh, Nellie. It's all too exciting. Last night Alexander declared his love for me. Well, at least he declared his love for the woman he knows who goes by the name of Arabella. But as soon as I let Arabella know what's happened he'll be declaring his love to a woman who goes by the name of Rosie,' She pointed to her chest. 'Me!'

Nellie stared at her, her face closed. It was not

the reaction Rosie had expected. Surely Nellie should be more excited and happy for her?

'Yes, I know who you are. I just hope the woman called Rosie knows what she's doing. The Duke may have fallen for you—I don't doubt that—but here you're Arabella: an heiress, the daughter of one of America's wealthiest men. Not a woman with no family and not a farthing to her name.'

Rosie frowned at Nellie, then shook her head, her smile returning. 'No, Nellie, you're wrong. Alexander's not like that. I *know* him. You don't. He didn't want to marry Arabella precisely *because* she's an heiress. He's too proud to take her father's money. He's a proud, honourable man.'

He was also handsome and could turn her to jelly with his kisses, she wanted to add as a shiver of remembered pleasure rippled through her body.

'Oh, Rosie, just don't get your hopes up too high—otherwise when you come crashing down to reality the fall might be more than you can cope with. Men like the Duke do *not* marry women like Rosie Smith.'

Rosie shook her head vehemently. 'No, you're wrong. He loves me. *Me*.' She pointed to her chest again. 'And that's all that matters.'

Nellie was wrong. Rosie knew it. She had seen how Alexander had looked at her last night. That had been the look of a man in love. In love with *her*. It hadn't been just passion she'd seen in his eyes, and it hadn't been just lust. It had been love. Real love.

Nellie sighed and shook her head slowly. 'Well, that's as may be, but hold still now while I get you dressed. Stop spinning round like a top.'

Rosie tried to remain still while Nellie helped her out of her nightdress and into her clothes, but it was too hard—she just wanted to dance and sing in celebration of the night before and the day that was to come.

Her desire to see Alexander again was overwhelming. She desperately wanted the day to begin so she could see his handsome face. But she also wanted the day to be over, so she could return to London as soon as possible and be set free from pretending to be Arabella, return to being Rosie Smith. Then Alexander could get to know the *real* Rosie—the Rosie that he had fallen in love with, the Rosie he had kissed, the Rosie he had caused to writhe in pleasure under his touch.

Then it really would be perfect.

There was no sign of Alexander in the hushed dining room. Only the Dowager and Charlotte were sitting at the highly polished walnut table, with matching grim expressions on their faces. It seemed last night's good grace between them had come to an end and they were once again adversaries.

Never mind. Rosie would talk to Charlotte when they spent time together this morning, and try and make things better between them. After all, wasn't she the breath of fresh air the servants said the family needed?

'Good morning…good morning,' she trilled, and headed towards the sideboard.

It seemed it was self-service this morning, as none of the usual bevy of servants were in attendance.

She lifted the lids of the silver tureens and was greeted by the delicious aromas of crisply fried bacon, scrambled eggs, fried mushrooms and tomatoes. The food looked delicious, and she had never been so hungry. It must be the excitement. Or perhaps being in love stimulated the appetite. Whatever it was, she needed food. Lots of it. Instead of her usual toast and marmalade, this morning she would treat herself to a full English breakfast.

Her plate piled high, she joined her future family at the table. Smiling, she removed her napkin from the engraved silver napkin ring and placed it on her lap. 'Isn't it a beautiful day?'

No greeting came from either woman. Instead the Dowager picked up the newspaper and gripped it tightly, as if frightened that it would fly out of her hands, and Charlotte stared down at her half-eaten plate of food, her shoulders slumped.

Rosie's smile faded. What was wrong? This was more than their usual ill humour towards each other. Had something happened to Alexander?

Rosie waited, looking from Charlotte to the Dowager and back again, but it seemed neither women felt compelled to enlighten her.

'A beautiful day, is it? I don't think so.' The Dowager finally snapped, her long bejewelled fingers twisting at the paper. 'Perhaps you'd like to explain *this*.'

The Dowager sent the newspaper skidding across the table in Rosie's direction. Rosie's hand shot out to stop it before it fell off the edge, and she looked down at the headline: *New Oscar Wilde Play a Resounding Success*.

'Is that not good news?' she asked, but got a scowl from the Dowager in response.

Perhaps the Dowager didn't approve of Oscar Wilde. Rosie had heard that some people objected to his somewhat flamboyant lifestyle, and the Dowager was hardly likely to be familiar with the ways of theatrical people.

'You have no shame, have you?' the Dowager shot back through clenched teeth.

Rosie sent the Dowager a questioning look, then continued reading the article, which discussed the intricacies of the storyline, the wonderful performances of the cast, and mentioned the series of standing ovations the play had received.

When she got to the bottom of the page she read a paragraph about the notable people who had attended the opening, including American heiress Arabella van Haven, who had dined with the playwright.

So Arabella had got her wish. She had attended the opening night of an Oscar Wilde play and had not only got to meet the great man himself but had actually dined with him. Wonderful.

Smiling, she looked up at the scowling Dowager and the frowning Charlotte—then looked back down at the newspaper.

'Oh,' she squeaked. 'I see…'

'Oh, indeed,' the Dowager said, standing and glaring down at Rosie.

'I can explain…'

Rosie bit the edge of her bottom lip. But what was she going to say? She could hardly tell them she was here taking her friend's place because Arabella would rather go to an Oscar Wilde play than attend their weekend house party, even if it *had* been hosted in her honour.

'Who are you? You're obviously not Arabella van Haven,' the Dowager thundered.

'Um… I'm…'

Where should Rosie begin? What could she possibly say to explain herself?

The Dowager Duchess held up her hands and turned her face away, as if repelled by even looking at Rosie. 'No, I don't want to know. You've lied to us already—as if I would believe anything you would say now. You come into my house... make a fool of me and my guests...insinuate your way into my son's affections... And now you think you can talk your way out of it. You're shameless.'

Rosie stood up, still clutching the newspaper. 'No—no, I didn't...'

She gripped the edge of the table, her mind spinning, her body feeling weak. She wanted to entreat the Dowager, to convince her that she'd meant no harm, but what could she say without betraying Arabella?

'The servants are packing your bags. I would not be so uncivil as to throw you out without your breakfast, but once you have finished eating *our* food—' she scowled at Rosie's laden plate '—the carriage will be ready to take you to the railway station. And that will be the end of it.'

'But Alexander? Where's Alexander? I need to speak to him.'

'As if my son would want to talk to a woman like *you*.'

'But I need to tell him—'

'You will tell him *nothing*. And if you have the slightest shred of decency you will tell no one about the way you have made complete fools of this family.'

The Dowager turned and walked towards the door.

'I didn't mean any harm!' Rosie called out to the retreating ramrod-straight back. 'It's just that I... The plan wasn't going to cause any harm... It was just to... I didn't mean to...'

Her hand on the doorknob, the Dowager stopped and turned back to Rosie. 'Stop talking, you thoughtless girl. I don't want to hear any more of your lies. Be thankful that I care about the good name of FitzRoy and want to avoid a scandal. If I didn't I would have you arrested for your fraudulent behaviour. Instead of catching the train home you would be spending the night in jail. And instead of eating that hearty breakfast you'd be dining on bread and water.'

'But I need to talk to Alexander—'

'Don't push me, girl. I can still change my mind and call for the constabulary. My son does not want to talk to you. *No one* wants to talk to you. Now, come, Charlotte, let's leave this criminal to fill her belly with *our* food.'

With that she left the room, followed by an obviously distressed Charlotte.

'But... But...' Rosie called out to the now closed

door. 'But I didn't mean any harm,' she said quietly, and then slumped down on to a dining chair, the crumpled newspaper still clutched in her hand.

Chapter Seventeen

It was all over. How could Alexander not hate her now? The Dowager had said he didn't want to talk to her. This was as bad as it could get.

How had everything gone so horribly wrong? Her plan had been simple enough: save Arabella from an unwanted marriage and have some fun at the same time by making fools of a greedy duke and his snobbish family. Then she would return to London with a funny story to tell Arabella—something that would amuse her just as so many of Rosie's antics had amused Arabella in the past.

But instead of making a fool of a stuffy duke, it was she who was the fool. Instead of having a joke at their expense, *she* was the joke.

She gripped both sides of her lowered head and released a deep sob. And now she would go home in disgrace. It was all too, too terrible. And, worse than that, she had caused the man she loved to despise her—had caused his family to think she was a fraudster instead of merely a silly, foolish girl who thought it was amusing to play tricks on people.

'Damn, damn, *damn*,' she cursed under her breath.

And the worst thing of all: her behaviour had hurt Alexander. His lasting memory of her would be as a liar, a woman up to no good, not a woman who loved him, a woman he had held in his arms and who had surrendered herself to his touch, to his kisses.

No, that could not happen.

Rosie stood up quickly, nearly toppling over the chair. She had to do something. She could not just sit there, wallowing in despair. There was no time to waste in self-indulgence. The carriage would be taking her away soon—taking her away from Alexander. Despite the Dowager's threats, she had to find him. She had to try and explain herself.

Even if it resulted in her being thrown in jail, she couldn't leave without talking to Alexander.

She ran out of the dining room, down the corridor, out through the entrance hall, and then halted at the top of the stairs, looking in every direction. Over the vast estate, at the gardens, the woodlands, the green pastures dotted with sheep.

Where would he be?

The door opened quietly behind her and she

turned expectantly. But instead of Alexander it was Charlotte, her mouth turned down in a frown, her shoulders slumped.

Intense shame swept over Rosie. Charlotte was hurt too. It had never been her intention to hurt anyone. But she had.

'Oh, Charlotte, I'm so sorry.' She reached her hands out towards the distressed young woman who had shown her nothing but friendship.

Charlotte took a step backwards, as if shocked by the gesture. 'It is unforgivable that you betrayed Alexander. He did not deserve to be betrayed again…to be lied to again.'

Tears filled Rosie's eyes. 'I know. I *know*. I want to apologise to him. I want to try and explain to him what I did and why I did it. Please, Charlotte, can you tell me where he is?'

Charlotte released a long sigh. 'I don't know who you are, or why you are here, but I do know my brother has fallen in love with you, and I do believe you have fallen in love with him. So if you want to talk to him you'll find him down by the river. There's a favourite place of his he used to go when he was a child. It's—'

'I know where it is!' Rosie called out, running down the stairs. 'And I'm sorry for everything I've done,' she shouted over her shoulder, while running along the pathway, her shoes crunching on the gravel.

Her mind spinning with half-formed explanations and excuses, she ran as fast as she could down the tree-lined path towards the river. How could she explain her behaviour? What could she say to him without betraying Arabella?

No answers came, but she had to think of something—had to say something. Had to make him see that she had meant no harm.

Surely when he saw her he would forgive her? After all, he had said he loved her, wanted to court her, even to marry her. And she was still the same woman he had declared his love for. That hadn't changed. Nothing had changed. Not really. It was just that she was not called Arabella and didn't really have a fortune, a rich father or a dowry.

Reaching the river, she came to an abrupt halt and stopped, giving herself time to catch her breath. As she approached the spot where yesterday they had skimmed stones with such childlike joy, she saw him sitting on the stone bench, staring into space.

In profile, his handsome face looked morose, and his body was rigid. Rosie's stomach clenched tightly with guilt. It was her fault he was in such pain. She had to put it right.

It had to be possible to change his mood. Wasn't that what she was good at? Making people laugh? Making them happy? She had spent most of her life entertaining Arabella, making her laugh when she was sad, lightening the mood in Mr van Haven's otherwise gloomy home. It was what she was best at.

But how?

For once she had no plan.

He turned his head slowly and stared up at her. His expression changed from sadness to impassiveness, as if he was shutting down all emotions. It was the same look she had seen the day they'd first met. Gone was the warmth in his brown eyes…gone was the loving look, the friendly smile.

Slowly, she walked towards him, her steps tentative, as if entering an ice-cold stream. When she was close to the bench he stood and faced her, his body tense, his face as harsh and bleak as a winter's storm.

'Oh, Alexander, I can explain…' She reached out to him.

He looked down at her hands, which remained suspended in mid-air between them, then back at her face, his eyes granite-hard. 'I'm sure you can, Miss van Haven—or whatever your real name is. I'm sure you have a very good explanation for why you deceived me, my family and our guests. You no doubt have a very plausible reason for your lies. Unfortunately for you I have been taken in by your lies once and I will not do it again.'

She slowly lowered her hands to her sides. 'Rosie—my name is Rosie.'

A sneer of contempt curled his lips. 'Rosie, Arabella—it makes no difference. Whoever you are, you are no longer welcome here. It is fortunate that your lies were exposed before the full extent of whatever crime you had planned was carried out.'

A gasp escaped Rosie's lips. 'No—*no!* There was no crime. You must believe that. Yes, I lied about who I am, but I meant no harm, and I was certainly never intending to commit a crime.'

Alexander glared down at her through narrowed eyes. 'How can you possibly think you would cause no harm? How could you possibly think that telling such lies, acting in such a manner, would not cause harm? Are you insane as well as deceitful?

Cringing at the insult, she reminded herself that he had every right to be angry with her. She would be angry if she thought he had lied to *her*. But she had to make him see that there had never been any ill intent behind her actions—quite the opposite. Perhaps her plan had been flawed, but how was she to have known that the stuffy, greedy Duke would be someone she would fall desperately in love with? If she had known that she would never have lied to him.

'I'm sorry. So very sorry. I know it was stupid

of me. And I'm very, very sorry. I intended telling you the truth—just not yet.'

He shook his head and laughed—a harsh, mirthless laugh. 'Oh, I *see*. Well, that makes everything all right, doesn't it? How could I possibly object if you were planning on telling the truth one day. So, when would that have been? When would you have told the truth? After we had married? When our first child was born? Or were you planning a deathbed confession?'

His sarcasm stung and she grew smaller under his withering stare. He could not think that of her. This had to be put right. But how?

Silently she asked for Arabella's forgiveness. There was no choice now but to tell Alexander who she really was. He already knew she wasn't Arabella, so it was time to tell the whole truth.

'I had intended to write to you after I got back to London, but I will tell you who I am now.'

He shook his head and gave a snort of sarcastic laughter. 'I can hardly wait…'

She forced herself to ignore the barb. 'My name is Rosie Smith. I'm Mr van Haven's ward and Arabella's friend. I'm not an heiress. In fact, I have no fortune of my own. I'm all but penniless.'

He stared at her for a moment, his disdain obvious. 'Yes, that I *do* believe.'

Rosie exhaled in relief and smiled slightly. He believed her. Thank goodness for that. Perhaps now they could put all this unpleasantness and these accusations behind them and return to the way they had been.

'An impoverished ward with ambitions to become a duchess? Yes, that makes perfect sense,' he sneered.

Her smile dissolved. 'No, I never had ambitions to—'

'It explains everything. Unfortunately, Rosie Smith, I have no interest in marrying an impoverished ward who uses such chicanery to advance her position in society. And I certainly have no respect for a woman who would use her *obvious* charms...' his dark eyes raked up and down her body '...to catch herself a titled husband.'

Rosie recoiled as if struck, blood rushing to her face, her heart pounding violently against the wall of her chest. 'How dare you?' she seethed through clenched teeth. 'How dare you accuse me of—?'

'I dare quite easily, Miss Smith. You have used the oldest tricks known to woman in order to ensnare a man. And I must say you are particularly adept at it.'

Rosie stared at him, uncharacteristically speechless, hardly able to believe what he was accusing her of. This was worse than his mother calling her a criminal. This was too bad.

How could he think that of her? He had ruined everything—tainted what had happened between them and reduced their affection, their passion and their love, to something sordid.

'No! *No!* It wasn't like that,' Rosie cried, barely able to hear her own voice above the sound of blood pounding in her ears. '*I'm* not like that,' she said, her voice rising. 'I wasn't trying to—'

Alexander glared down at her, his merciless eyes burning into hers, his lips a thin, disgusted line. 'That's exactly what it was like, Miss Smith. That's exactly what you were trying to do, and that's exactly the sort of woman you are. But this time you failed. Perhaps you'll have better luck next time and you'll be able to get some other hapless aristocrat to drag you out of the gutter and give you a title.'

Rosie felt her eyes grow wide and her mouth drop open. It seemed Nellie was right. Now that he knew who she really was he thought he was too good for her. As Nellie had said, men like him did not marry women like her. But that did not mean he had the right to insult her.

She closed her mouth, tilted her chin and glared back at him. 'You are an appalling man. You might be a duke but you are most certainly not a gentleman if you think you can speak to a lady like that. How I ever could have thought you were honourable and kind, I don't know.'

'Honourable? Kind?' He gave another humourless laugh. 'I don't think *those* were the attributes you were after. A title and a position in society? Weren't those the qualities you were looking for in a man?'

'I couldn't care less about your title,' Rosie fired back. 'I couldn't care less if you can trace your family back to the Stone Age. But it seems you do care. You think that because you've got a title, all this land and your fancy house, that you're better than me and you can talk to me any way you want.'

'I'm afraid, Miss Smith, your behaviour this weekend has shown that I *am* better than you. You're a liar and a charlatan who isn't above using her body for financial gain. And there are some *very* unpleasant names to describe a woman like that.'

'You—! You—!' Pain surged through Rosie as she clenched her hands so tightly her nails dug into her palms. She stared up at him, attempting to catch her breath as she tried to think of a way to wipe that arrogant sneer off his face.

Forcing herself to unclench her hands, she looked down at the ground and took a few steadying breaths. Slowly she raised her head, pulled herself up to her full height and stared him straight in the eye.

'Perhaps I have told a lie or two, but you're rude, insulting and a snob,' she hissed.

She had hoped her insult would affect him, but

he stared back at her with eyes as cold and dark as a winter sky.

'And *you*, Miss Smith, are a liar and a wh—'

'I am no such thing!' Rosie interjected, even though it meant lying again. Of course she had lied—but that wasn't the point, was it? It didn't mean he could talk to her in such a disrespectful manner or question her morality.

'All right—all right, I lied. And I've said I'm sorry about that. But you have no right to accuse me of…to accuse me of…'

'To accuse you of being a tart? A strumpet? A hussy? What word is it that you're searching for, Miss Smith? There are so many words available to describe a woman who uses her body to get what she wants.'

Her jaw and hands clenching tightly, Rosie glared up at his arrogant face. 'You contemptible man. To think I actually thought that I was in love with you. How could I have been so stupid as to think I loved a man as detestable as you? If I never see you again it will be far too soon.'

'Well, it seems there is one thing on which we are in complete agreement. I suggest you leave immediately and stop wasting my time.'

Rosie stared at him, her face burning, every muscle in her body clenched. There was so much more she wanted to say to him—so many more insults she wanted to fling in his direction. But what was the point? His arrogance was impenetrable. Nothing she could say would make any difference to his low opinion of her.

Summoning up as much dignity as possible, she turned abruptly and strode up the path, her skirts whipping around her ankles. As she walked quickly towards the carriage waiting outside the house a light rain started to fall, the raindrops merging with the tears of anger, shame and remorse running down her cheeks…

Chapter Eighteen

Pebble-sized circles formed on the river as raindrops hit the water, but Alexander was oblivious to the change in the weather. Nor did he hear the burbling river as it raced over the mossy rocks. With his mind shrouded in a fog of anger everything around him was all but silent and invisible.

Yes, he was angry. Angry with Miss Rosie Smith, or whoever she was, but he was even more angry with himself.

Angry that he could be so gullible. He had fallen for her lies, for her beauty, for her playacting. Hadn't he learnt his lesson with Lydia? It would appear not. The next pretty liar who had come his way had bewitched him and he had fallen again—fallen even harder this time.

He picked up a willow stick and whipped it against the nearest tree, trying to beat out the pain that had overtaken him. His pain over Lydia's betrayal had been intense, but it had been nothing like this. It had not been so all-consuming.

He had trusted her, this Miss Rosie Smith. He had believed her. Believed her lies. He had let down his guard—the guard that Lydia had taught him was essential if he was to avoid being betrayed again. And this was how his trust had been repaid.

Pain and anger continued to wage a war inside him as he walked up and down the edge of the river, determined to quash down all emotion. Anger he could cope with. Almost. But the pain—that was unbearable.

And he had a right to be angry. Everything about her had been a lie. She had even had the audacity to attempt to explain her actions. As if *anything* could explain her lies, her betrayal. And he had almost been taken in by them. For one fateful moment when he had seen her standing beside the river looking so forlorn he had wanted to *comfort* her.

He was a fool—a complete fool.

He hit the stick against the tree—harder. He knew what it was to be lied to repeatedly. Hadn't Lydia used exactly the same tricks? Hadn't Lydia said anything, done anything, to try and free herself from the web of lies she had woven around her? And he had believed her again and again, until it had been impossible to believe one more lie.

Well, not this time. Miss Rosie Smith had lied. She was a liar. That was all he needed to know. He did not need to know why she had lied or what her intentions had been. She was a liar. And he had been betrayed. *Again.*

Lydia's betrayal had been a mere bee-sting compared to the knife in the heart inflicted by Miss Smith. With Lydia he had never felt such all-consuming passion—a passion he could have drowned in, that could have taken him over and swept him away, so all he could think about was her, a woman he didn't even really know.

Yes, he was a fool. He had fallen in love with a chimera—a woman who didn't really exist. A woman who had been created as a device to ensnare him.

And she had almost succeeded.

Who she really was, what she was really like, he would never know. Never wanted to know.

An image of her laughing face and sad eyes entered his mind and his anger subsided slightly. He had never learnt why there was such sadness behind her laughter. Perhaps it was simply because she was poor and wanted a position in society.

He grabbed both ends of the willow stick and broke it in two. No, he did not need to know about her sadness. Did not need to know anything about her. She was gone and he had been saved from making even more of a fool of himself than he already had.

And yet here he was, standing by the river like some love-struck youth. He just had to remember that the woman he'd thought he loved did not exist.

Alexander tossed the sticks into the stream, watched them float away with the current, then turned and walked back towards the house. It was time to put this entire unfortunate incident behind him. He had work to do, and he had allowed himself to become distracted for far too long.

He should not be wasting time wallowing in self-pity. He should not be thinking about that woman—should not be remembering how she'd looked in the candlelight, or how her lips had felt on his, or what it had felt like to hold her in his arms. No, he should not think of such things. And he wouldn't ever again. Nor would he remember the sweet taste of her soft pink lips, the way she smelt of spring flowers, or how she looked when she lost herself in the passion of their embrace.

Instead he would write to the engineers tomorrow. They would begin draining the marshlands and that neglected area would be converted to farmland. He would arrange a loan with the bank to buy a steam-driven harvester, so the next harvest could be brought in more efficiently. He would contact the owners of the local railway company and begin discussions on bringing the line through his land. He would even investigate the possibility of introducing electricity to the dairy and woolsheds.

He stopped walking. Hadn't electrification been *her* suggestion?

Dragging in a deep breath, he strode off towards the house. It was of no matter where the idea had come from. He had much more important things to occupy his mind than thinking about that woman, or dwelling on such fripperies as her beauty, or how she played the piano with such passion, or how lovely her singing voice was.

He increased his walking pace. No, he would not think of such frivolous things—not when he had so much work to do.

As he neared the house Charlotte raced out to meet him, clutching a large black umbrella, her face contorted with worry.

She handed the umbrella to Alexander and he gripped the curved cane handle in a tight fist, sheltering his sister from the increasing downpour.

'Oh, Alexander, I'm so sorry. I know she meant so much to you.'

Anger continued to simmer inside him. That woman had also caused pain to his sister—a woman who had never hurt anyone.

He took her arm and patted her hand gently.

'It's all right, Charlotte. I'm all right. Please, I think it best if we just try and pretend none of this ever happened.'

'But what did she *say*? Why did she pass herself off as an American heiress? What was it all about?'

Charlotte clutched his arm, her questions coming in a rush, her eyes pleading with him.

'I have no idea, Charlotte. I'm just pleased that she has gone,' he said, his words more clipped than he intended.

'But didn't you ask her? Didn't you want to know? Didn't you *need* to know?'

Alexander released a sigh and looked over Charlotte's head into the distance. 'No, I didn't ask her. I neither needed nor wanted to know why she tried to trick me into marrying her. She's gone. There's no more to be said about it.'

Charlotte inhaled deeply, then slowly released her breath. 'You asked her to marry you? You really were in love with her, weren't you, Alexander? Oh, Alexander, surely you need to know why she did it?'

Alexander gripped the umbrella more tightly, his teeth clenched so firmly his jaw ached.

'If only you had asked, Alexander—asked her why she lied. Perhaps there was a good reason,' Charlotte said, her voice softening.

He looked down at his sister, her face pinched

with concern. But it was misdirected concern. Like him, Charlotte needed to forget all about Miss Rosie Smith.

'There can be no good reason to excuse her lies, her deception,' he said, keeping his voice even so his anger would not upset her.

Charlotte shook her head. 'I can't accept that, Alexander. She was here for only two days, and in those two short days she changed you. Because of her you opened up your heart—a heart that had been closed since Lydia left. Please, Alexander, don't just dismiss her…don't close down your heart again. You deserve to be happy—and Arabella, or whoever she is, made you happy.'

Alexander shook his head and exhaled loudly. His ever-perceptive sister was right. Thanks to Miss Rosie Smith he had opened his heart—and look what had happened. For that, he would never forgive her. He had felt so many emotions over the last two days—emotions he'd thought he had forgotten how to feel. And now all he was left with was anger and pain.

Charlotte released her grip on his arm and lightly patted it. 'Perhaps when you calm down you should contact her and find out why she lied to us.'

'No, Charlotte,' he said through gritted teeth, to stop himself from shouting. 'I will *not* be contacting her, and I forbid you from having anything to do with her.'

Charlotte tilted her head and raised her eyebrows.

Alexander knew he had made a mistake. The best way to get Charlotte to want to do something was to forbid it.

'I'm sorry, Charlotte,' he said, his voice softening. 'I did not mean to lose my temper with you. But I entreat you to leave this alone. Nothing good will come of contacting that woman.'

Before she could formulate any other arguments he took her arm and walked her towards the house. He knew he would have to speak to Charlotte again on the subject at a later date because, like his mother, once her mind was made up it could be a monumental challenge to get her to change it.

And the last thing he wanted was for her to have any contact with Miss Rosie Smith.

Chapter Nineteen

Being a strong and resourceful woman was something Rosie had always prided herself on. She'd had to be strong when her father had died. She'd had to be even stronger when her mother had died and she'd been left all alone in the world. She'd had to be strong to endure being poor in a world of extreme wealth, and she'd had to be strong to cope with being completely dependent on Mr van Haven's reluctant charity.

Now she had to be even stronger. She had to be brave and to appear unaffected by the reality that she had fallen in love with a man who now despised her...who thought she was an immoral, gold-digging con woman.

When she'd returned to London she had resolved to keep what had happened a secret from Arabella. All her friend needed to know was that she was safe and did not have to marry the Duke.

Arabella did not need to be upset by the painful details.

All her life Rosie had tried to repay her debt to Arabella by entertaining her, keeping her happy, distracting her from the sense of neglect she felt as a result of her father's constant absences. And that was what she intended to do now.

Arabella was trying to establish her career on the stage and that was all that mattered. Rosie would force herself to be happy, to smile, to laugh. After all, wasn't that what she always did? Kept smiling no matter what. Even if her heart was breaking.

Her tea whirled round and round in her cup as she continued to stir long after the sugar had dissolved, the spoon clinking against the fine bone china. Yes, she had to be strong for herself and also for Arabella.

Things were going so well for Arabella. While Rosie took afternoon tea Arabella was attending an audition for a play being staged by a small, newly formed London theatre. She was so close to achieving her dream of becoming an actress, and Rosie would not burden her with her own problems.

She was happy for her friend—very happy. And once that vicarious happiness would have been enough. Not long ago all she had ever wanted was for her best friend to achieve her dreams. She owed so much to the kind and generous young woman who had saved her from a life of poverty and vulnerability on the streets of New York. Just a few short days ago she had been prepared to dedicate the rest of her life to being Arabella's companion, and that ambition had been more than enough for her.

That was until she had met Alexander FitzRoy, Lord Ashton, the Eighth Duke of Knightsbrook. He had turned her world upside down and had changed everything.

Now she had to fight so hard to keep smiling that her cheeks often ached with the strain. It was becoming increasingly difficult to stop the edges of her lips from trembling, to stop her misery breaking through the veneer of joy she was determined to maintain.

Rosie released a quiet sigh. She lifted the teacup to her lips, then lowered it again, un-tasted, and tried to take comfort in the fact that her plan had actually succeeded. At least she had achieved her goal, she thought with sardonic humour.

She had arrived at Knightsbrook with the intention of behaving so badly that Alexander and the FitzRoys would eventually drive her out of the house, never wanting to see her again. And she had succeeded.

She lifted the cup once more to her lips, took a sip, but tasted nothing of the now cold tea. Yes, she deserved the pain she was feeling. Her actions had been appalling. She had lied to Alexander, betrayed his trust and the trust of his family. Charlotte had been right. Alexander did not deserve to be treated in such a manner. Another deep blush of shame swept over her. He deserved someone so much better than her.

Arabella entered the Palm Court at The Ritz, her charming demeanour and pretty face causing every head in the room to turn in her direction. She made her way between the tables, her face a beaming smile, her eyes sparkling.

Rosie forced herself to sit up straighter and to adopt her sunniest smile.

'I got the part! I can't believe it, but I did it—I got the part. I'm going to appear on the London stage!' Arabella nodded her thanks to the waiter who was pulling out her chair and sat down, still smiling. 'It's just a small part, but it's mine, and I appear in virtually every scene.'

'Oh, Bella, that's wonderful news,' Rosie said, clapping her hands together. 'Congratulations! You deserve it. You really are very talented.'

Arabella signalled to the waiter for afternoon tea, pulled off her gloves, clasped her hands together and placed them on the table. 'So… I think I've given you enough time,' she said, her face becoming serious. 'If you're not going to volunteer to tell me, then I'm just going to have to ask you. What's wrong, Rosie? Why are you so unhappy?'

Rosie shook her head and forced her smile to grow even larger. 'Nothing's wrong. I—'

'Don't tell me that nothing's wrong, Rosie. You've been miserable since you came back from Knightsbrook. I know you think it's your role to be the happy one, to entertain me. You've always been like that since we were young girls. But I don't want any more of your fake smiles and pretend joyfulness. What happened? Were they really mean to you?'

Rosie's mouth turned down and she shook her head. 'No, they were lovely.'

'Oh… Was the Duke stuffy and unbearable?'

'No, no… He was actually rather nice. Handsome, kind, honourable—not stuffy at all.'

Arabella gave her an assessing stare and Rosie's cheeks burned more fiercely.

'Oh, Rosie. Is that what the problem is? Was he *very* nice, *very* handsome, *very* kind and honourable?

Rosie nodded.

'And has he captured your heart?'

She nodded again.

'And was he uninterested because you have no money of your own?'

Rosie shook her head, then remembered what Nellie had said about aristocratic men not marrying out of their class and nodded. But she was sure Nellie was wrong, so she shook her head again.

'I don't think such things matter to Alexander.'

'Then what went wrong? Why was he uninterested? Is the man a simpleton? You're beautiful, funny, charming. If you set your mind to it no man could resist you.'

'Oh, Bella. You're so kind.' Tears welled up in Rosie's eyes. 'But it's not that straightforward. He *was* interested. In fact he said he loved me, said he wanted to marry me—but that was when he thought I was *you*.'

Arabella tilted her chin and narrowed her eyes. 'So it *was* money he was after. Well, you're better off without him.'

'No, no, Arabella. You don't understand. He never wanted to marry you—well, at least he never wanted your money…never wanted to marry for money. He's a fiercely proud man, and even though the FitzRoys have lost their wealth he wants to restore the family fortune and their good name through hard work—not by marrying an heiress.'

'Well, there's no problem, then.' Arabella gave a little laugh. 'You have no money of your own. You're exactly what he's after.'

Rosie shrugged and sighed. 'Except he's also an honourable man. When he found out I'd lied to him by pretending to be someone else he was furious. He saw what I'd done as unforgivable.'

'But surely when you told him *why* you were lying he must have understood? Surely an honourable man would know that if you're lying to save someone else then it's not an unforgivable action.'

Rosie looked down at her teacup and then back up at Arabella. 'I didn't tell him why I was pretending to be you. At first it was because I didn't want to betray you. And then I got so angry… I said some terrible things to him that just confirmed all the bad things he thought about me. And then he got angry with me and said some awful things back. And then we both said we never wanted to see each other again. And then I left.'

'Oh.'

'Yes. *Oh.*'

The waiter served Arabella's tea. She spooned several sugars into her cup and began stirring. 'So what's your plan? How are you going to win him back?'

Rosie stared wide-eyed at her friend. 'What? I have no "plan". Well, the only plan I have is to forget all about it eventually. I'm sure when enough time has passed I won't even remember what he looked like.'

Rosie gave a tentative smile and placed a

smoked salmon sandwich on her plate, although eating was the last thing she felt like doing.

Arabella stopped stirring and placed her tea-spoon on her saucer, her pretty mouth turned down. 'Hmm… You really are in a bad state, aren't you? When have you ever *not* had a plan? You're a fighter, Rosie. You don't give up easily. You never have before and this is not the time to start.'

Rosie shrugged again. 'You can't *make* some-one love you, Bella. All I seem to have done is a very good job of making Alexander hate me.'

'I'm sure that's not true,' Arabella said, shaking her head. 'If he said he loved you once then I'm sure you can make him see that he still loves you—even if you're not who you said you were, and even if you did tell him a few innocent fibs.'

Rosie held up her hands. It was time to end this uncomfortable conversation. 'I know you mean well, Bella, but there's nothing to be done. Alexander is in the past, and I think it would be best if that's where he stays.' She forced another smile. 'So, tell me about this play—what part did you get? Let's start reading lines together after tea, so you're word-perfect for the first rehearsal.'

As long as she kept her mind occupied Rosie was certain that eventually, in time, Alexander would stop monopolising her daytime thoughts and her night-time dreams.

Arabella stared at her for a moment, her brows drawn together in question. 'Right...and once we've done that we'll get down to formulating a plan to recapture the Duke's heart.'

Rosie stifled a sigh. Arabella had the best of intentions, but this time there would be no plan. It was time to admit defeat. It was time to forget Alexander. It was time to move on.

Alexander looked out at the marshlands. After many days' work alongside the engineers and workmen the trenches had been dug and draining the area would soon commence, so that it could be turned into productive farmland. It should be a satisfying sight. He had secured good terms with the bank to pay for the work and had finally started on his plans to transform and modernise the estate.

And yet he was far from satisfied. Discontent racked his mind, and despite his tired muscles his body continued to be in a state of agitation.

He had laboured hard beside his tenants, digging from sun-up to sun-down, trying to exhaust his body so he would fall into a dreamless sleep at night. But still thoughts of a raven-haired beauty had invaded his dreams. And she was constantly on his waking mind, no matter how many distractions he placed in his own way.

He walked along the edge of the marshland, his

boots squelching through thick mud. Their final encounter played over in his head once again. How he regretted his cruel words. He should never have flung those insulting names at her. He had no real evidence that she was an immoral woman.

He stopped and stared out at the boggy land. If he could take those harsh words back he would—in a second. But he couldn't undo what had been done. He'd thought of sending her an apology, but he had vowed to himself that he would have no contact with her, and he doubted she'd want any contact with him.

Anyway, what would be gained by an apology?

What would be gained by making contact?

And if he did apologise what would he say?

How could he explain that he had lashed out like an injured animal, thrashing about without thought, only aware that he was in pain and that he would do anything, say anything, to make the pain stop?

He picked up a stick and poked it into the damp earth.

But there had been one good outcome of her visit. She had been right about those plans to diversify. It had been that which had convinced the bank to lend him a substantial amount of money. They had been able to see the good business sense in producing a diversity of crops that could be transported by rail around the country and even abroad. And it had been her suggestion of electrification that had sealed the deal.

He had hoped that the whole unfortunate incident would put his mother off her quest to find a future duchess with a substantial dowry, but it had not been the case.

His mother was wasting her time. Alexander could not see himself taking an interest in any other woman—not when he found it impossible to get Rosie Smith out of his mind. He would always compare all others to her, and he could not imagine meeting another woman who was as funny, as pretty and such a delight.

Although how much of her charm had been real and how much of it pretence he had no way of gauging. But the woman she had pretended to be—the one who had made him laugh, who had made him forget himself and his troubles—was one he had so easily fallen in love with.

It seemed Rosie Smith had ruined his chances with any other woman. He had fallen in love with a charade, and no real woman would ever be able to match her.

He pulled the stick out of the sucking mud and threw it into the marshland. It was time to be true to his commitment and force himself to excise her from his mind. It might take a while to get her out of his thoughts, but that was what he must do.

And hopefully one day, some time in the distant future, he would have forgotten what she even looked like, forgotten her voice and the pretty laughter that came so easily, forgotten those disconcertingly sad blue eyes.

He had plenty of other things to occupy his thoughts. His negotiations with the railway were going well, and preparation of the land where the tracks would be laid would soon start. Once again he planned to join in with the men and help in the clearance of the land. He enjoyed the easy camaraderie of his tenants, and the feeling of pushing himself with hard physical labour.

He turned and headed back to the house. His muscles ached from the hard day's work, and that at least gave him some satisfaction. Tomorrow would be another day of constant activity, and tonight he would bury himself in plans for the railway. As long as he was making plans for the estate and throwing himself into hard physical toil he could hopefully keep all invading thoughts of a pretty, tormenting, deceitful American at bay.

At least, that was the plan.

Chapter Twenty

Rosie needed time—that much she knew. But how much time?

That was a question she couldn't begin to answer. How long did it actually take for a broken heart to mend? Perhaps she should consult a doctor, because no one else seemed to know. And while that elusive amount of time was passing what was she supposed to do to ease her pain? How was she supposed to remove the constant memory of her last encounter with Alexander from her mind? How was she supposed to stop recalling all those other bittersweet memories of how he looked, how he talked, how his face changed when he laughed and, most painful of all, how his lips felt on hers?

She wandered aimlessly around the hotel suite, picked up a pen from the writing desk, twirled it in her fingers, then put it down again. She moved to the floor-to-ceiling windows. Outside there was a bustling city, just waiting for her to explore.

She pulled back the chintz drapes and looked down at the smartly dressed men and women walking along the pavement below, at the roads congested with horses and carts delivering goods to the many stores, and the carriages and omnibuses ferrying busy people to their destinations. Strains of music from the organ grinder at the street corner reached her.

There was so much activity just outside the front door of her hotel and she should be a part of it—not merely staring down at it from on high, like some miserable princess trapped in a tower.

Yes, she had to move on. Like the organ grinder's handle, the world kept on turning—so she should get out, leave the hotel and join in with that world.

She released the curtains, the mere thought of it draining her of energy.

The door burst open and Arabella swept in, waving tickets above her head. 'Right, you've been moping too long. It's time we went out and enjoyed ourselves. I've got tickets to the Gaiety Theatre on Saturday night. Rumour has it that Lillie Langtry is going to be putting in a guest appearance, so that is one performance we cannot miss. Nellie's going to make us both look beautiful, and Aunt Prudence says she's recovered and can accompany us—so no excuses. You're going to have some *fun*.'

Rosie forced her lips to smile. 'That's wonderful, Bella, how exciting,' she said, with more enthusiasm than she felt.

Just a few short weeks ago the idea of going to the Gaiety Theatre would have filled her with genuine excitement. And actually seeing the famous actress and socialite Lillie Langtry on stage would have been a dream come true. But now she was having to force herself to summon up even a modicum of enthusiasm.

She looked at her smiling friend and realised Arabella was right. She had to shake off this wretched misery, if for no other reason than she didn't want her sadness to make Arabella unhappy as well.

'In the meantime there's shopping to be done,' Arabella continued. 'We'll both need new gowns, new shoes, new hats, new evening bags—new everything if we're to attend the theatre. Plus, we've been very remiss in our exploration of London. We haven't yet visited any of the department stores. I've been dying to see inside the new Harrods. They say it's been rebuilt in spectacular fashion since the fire. It's the largest store in Europe, so it should have everything we could possibly need, and more, all under one roof. We can spend the day there, buy everything we need, and then when we're exhausted with shopping we can take afternoon tea to replenish ourselves for more shopping!'

Rosie smiled her first genuine smile for many days. It was usually her job to make Arabella feel happy, to entertain her friend—not the other way around. But her dear friend was doing everything she could to divert Rosie from her sorrows. Arabella truly was a good friend. The best friend a woman could ever have.

'Thank you, Bella, that sounds wonderful.'

'Oh, don't thank me. Just get ready and join me down in the foyer as quickly as possible. We're on a mission. There's much to do, many items to buy, and no time to waste.'

The two girls stepped down from their hansom cab, stood in front of Harrods and stared up at its seven-storey exterior. It was indeed spectacular, combining the modern American concept of a department store with a British sense of elegance. Adorned with cherubs and its new modern Art Nouveau windows, it seemed to draw them in with the promise of luxury and indulgence.

Inside it was no less spectacular, and the two girls were instantly absorbed into the hubbub of excited shoppers. As they rushed from counter to counter, trying on hats, gloves and scarves, sampling perfumes and watching elegant models display the latest fashions, Rosie was almost able to forget her sadness. *Almost*.

It was just unfortunate that she kept seeing Alexander among the bustling crowd, and then realising she was wrong. The breadth of one man's shoulders reminded her of Alexander's strong physique, but when he turned round it wasn't his handsome face she saw but that of a complete stranger. Another man held his head erect in just the same manner as Alexander, but when he looked her way she was again disappointed.

This was silly, she reminded herself. Alexander was in Devon. She would never see him again and she had to put him out of her mind.

Which was an equally silly idea. Rosie knew she would *never* be able to put Alexander out of her mind.

But at least she could keep trying. Even if she failed again and again and again.

After a whirl of shopping—broken only by a stop for afternoon tea—a hansom cab was summoned to take them back to the hotel, along with their many carefully wrapped packages.

Rosie had expected to return to the hotel suite to have a much-needed rest. But Arabella had other ideas. It seemed she had prepared a full itinerary of activities to keep every minute of Rosie's day and evening occupied.

Her friend knew her so well. Without these activities Rosie knew she would sink back into her morose state. So Arabella had deemed that there would not be a minute left for Rosie to sit staring out of the window of her London hotel, dwelling on what had happened with Alexander.

'Look what I've got.'

Alexander raised his head, tearing his eyes away from the sorry tale told by the estate's financial ledgers, and gazed at his smiling sister. She was standing at the door of his office, holding a torn envelope and waving two pieces of paper.

'I've got tickets to the Gaiety Theatre on Saturday night.'

'I'm very pleased for you,' he said absentmindedly, placing his hands on the desk and returning his attention to the dilemma of how to save costs on the estate's expenditure without losing any workers.

'They're for us. We need to get out of this dismal house for a few days. We need to go up to London for the weekend. We need to have some fun for a change.'

Frowning, Alexander scrutinised his sister. *Fun?* This was not like Charlotte. The only time she went up to London was when she was visiting one of her charities, or attending a political meeting. When had she ever wanted to do something frivolous like seeing a play? Next thing she would be saying she actually *enjoyed* going to balls.

'I'm far too busy, Charlotte. And we can't spend money on plays and trips to London. We need to cut back on expenses—not waste money.'

Charlotte entered the room, slammed the tickets down on the desk and furrowed her brow.

Startled by this uncharacteristic display of anger, Alexander looked up at her.

'You're not too busy, and it won't cost us much. We can stay at our London townhouse. It will be good to make use of it one last time before you sell it. And you'll only be away for a few days. You deserve a break after all your hard work and everything you've been through.'

'No, Charlotte.'

'*Yes, Charlotte.* That's the response you're meant to give. If you won't do it for yourself then do it for me. You've been such a misery to live with these past few weeks. You might enjoy being miserable, but I don't like being subjected to all this gloom and doom. I need cheering up as well, you know. So do it for me.'

He stared at his sister. What was happening to her? Was she having a kind of personality change? Insisting on having fun one moment and admonishing him the next. Perhaps his miserable countenance *had* been adversely affecting her, causing her to behave strangely. And she did deserve to have some fun after Miss Smith's betrayal and the uncertainty of their financial woes.

'All right,' he said slowly. 'I suppose one weekend won't hurt. And if you're prepared to waste your allowance on tickets to the theatre, then I suppose I can waste a bit of money on train tickets to London.'

'Good—that's settled.' Charlotte walked away, humming the chorus of 'Champagne Charlie'.

Alexander shuddered at the sound of the tune Miss Smith had entertained them with. He did not need reminding of her. He did not need reminding of all the damage she had caused. He did not need reminding of the pain he had felt—the pain he had been forced to crush down inside him until it sat in his stomach like a lead weight.

He turned back to his ledger, found the figures swirling before his eyes. He had to concentrate. He could not let her invade his mind again and distract him from the important work he had to do. She had taken up too much of his time and his thoughts already.

He would not think of her. He would drive all memories of her from his head. He closed his eyes, took in a deep breath, then stared back at the accounts, forcing himself to concentrate. He could not be distracted—especially if he was going to waste an entire weekend on a visit to London...

* * *

Arabella was bubbling with eager anticipation as they headed towards the Gaiety Theatre, and Rosie couldn't help but get caught up in her excitement. Even Aunt Prudence seemed to have brightened up a bit. After spending several weeks in bed, recovering from her imagined sea sickness and then a bout of hay fever, followed by an unidentified malaise, she had finally dragged herself out of her sickbed to fulfil her role as chaperon.

Rosie watched the busy London streets pass them by as the carriage clip-clopped along the cobbled road. Lit up by the gas lamps and the soft white light of a full moon, London looked spectacular.

When they arrived at the Gaiety Theatre their driver jostled with other coach drivers, all dropping off their cargo of excited theatregoers. With careful manoeuvring he managed to find a spot right outside the covered front entrance, so the ladies could disembark comfortably.

'Oh, dear. It's very noisy, isn't it?' Aunt Prudence complained as they entered the foyer. 'I hope it doesn't bring on one of my headaches.'

Rosie and Arabella looked at each other and giggled. *Everything* tended to bring on one of Aunt Prudence's imagined headaches.

But she was right about one thing. The crowded foyer presented a wall of sound, with a mass of bejewelled women and men in formal evening wear talking loudly, laughing and greeting their friends. There was a palpable buzz of excitement, and the rumour that Lillie Langtry might be making a guest appearance had obviously spread, because every group they passed seemed to be talking of her.

The girls made their way up the wide, richly carpeted stairs, along the corridors, and found their box. When they entered their own exclusive little room the noise of the crowd dimmed slightly.

Rosie seated herself and looked out on the assembled audience. The patrons in the stalls below bustled and jostled as they found their seats. In the rows of boxes across from them wealthy patrons entered at a more leisurely pace and settled themselves in for the night's entertainment.

'If Lillie Langtry is going to be on stage, then perhaps the Prince of Wales will attend as well,' Arabella said, scanning her programme. 'They say that she's his mistress, and he *is* rather partial to actresses. Perhaps when I become a famous actress I should become his mistress. I wonder what Father would prefer? Me being the future King's mistress or the wife of an aristocrat.'

Rosie looked at her giggling friend. It wasn't like Arabella to make fun of the way her father was using her to advance his own social status. She was obviously in a very good mood tonight.

The door to their box opened.

Rosie and Arabella turned as a smiling Charlotte FitzRoy entered. Rosie shook her head in bewilderment, as if an apparition had suddenly appeared, and then her heart plummeted to her stomach when she heard a familiar deep voice.

'Charlotte, what are you up to? I don't believe your meagre allowance could possibly stretch to taking a box. Are you sure our tickets aren't for the stalls?' said Alexander as he followed his sister into the box, looking down at the tickets and scowling.

When he looked up and saw Rosie staring at him he halted, his face wary, like a man suddenly aware he was entering an ambush. And that was exactly what this was.

Rosie looked from Charlotte to Arabella, then back again. They were wearing identical smiles. This encounter was obviously not a bizarre co-incidence. It was something Arabella and Charlotte had concocted.

'Hello, I'm Arabella van Haven—the real Arabella van Haven,' her friend said, standing and smiling like Alice's Cheshire Cat. 'Rosie you already know, and may I present my aunt? Miss Prudence van Haven.'

Alexander stared at them for a moment, as if

too stunned to talk, then his well-conditioned manners took over and he bowed to all three women. 'And may I present my sister? Lady Charlotte.'

'It's a pleasure to meet you, Lady Charlotte,' Arabella said, taking Charlotte's arm and leading her to a seat beside her.

The two women commenced chattering enthusiastically, as if oblivious to the tense atmosphere that had now descended on the box.

Rosie remained frozen in her seat, staring up at an equally stunned Alexander. For several painful seconds they remained motionless, like prey caught in a snare and unable to make any move to get free without fear of ensnaring themselves further.

'I'm sorry about this, Alexander,' she said finally, her voice a small croak. 'I didn't know a thing about it. I know you think I'm a liar, but you have to believe me. This is not my doing.'

'Oh, I do believe you. I can see the hand of my sister at work here.'

Rosie nodded. 'And my friend Arabella. The real Arabella. But you're here now. You might as well enjoy the play.'

He cast an annoyed glance at his sister and entered the box.

Rosie had almost forgotten how very handsome he was. Tall, and with such wide shoulders and dark good looks that he was nothing short of stunning. And seeing him again had certainly left *her* stunned.

But as he approached she became aware of a change in his appearance. There were dark rings under his eyes, and a sallowness to his olive skin that hadn't been there when she had visited Knightsbrook. He gave every appearance of a man who had not been sleeping properly.

Had he been working too hard? Worrying about the estate? Whatever had caused this change in him Rosie wanted to help, to soothe away his worries, to brush back the dark brown hair from his furrowed forehead. But caring for the Duke was not her role. It never had been and never would be.

He hesitated, then walked towards the one remaining seat—the seat beside Rosie.

Time seemed to slow down. The tension between them grew. The very air seemed heavy, and Rosie struggled to breathe. The noisy crowd fell silent. It was as if every member of the audience was aware of Rosie's embarrassment and discomfort, and were waiting with bated breath to see what happened next.

Arabella patted her arm. 'Rosie, stand up. The Prince of Wales is here.'

Rosie turned in her seat and as if through a haze of confusion saw a portly gentleman with a full beard enter the royal box. She gathered herself and stood up as Alexander reached his seat and stood beside her.

Someone in the crowd shouted out, 'Three cheers for His Royal Highness,' and they all joined in on three hearty 'hip-hip-hoorays'. All except Rosie and Alexander, whose somewhat muted responses were fortunately drowned out by the happy crowd.

How could Rosie be expected to cheer when she was in a state of shock? When her skin was tingling with nerves and her throat was so constricted she suspected she was incapable of speech?

The band struck up a lively tune and the audience took their seats again. Rosie closed her eyes to try and regain some composure. But how was she supposed to do that in this impossible situation? The man she had thought she would never see again was now sitting close beside her. The man she had treated so badly, the man she had lied to and insulted, the man she had fallen in love with, was now just a few inches away from her.

Rosie wriggled slightly in her seat to try and move away from Alexander, but the arrangement of the chairs allowed no room. A chill ran through her, as if the temperature had suddenly plummeted in the warm theatre. The naked skin of her arms and shoulders tingled, and she was aware that she was all but brushing up against his arm and shoulder. Her leg was so close to his they were almost touching.

She looked down at his legs and could see the muscles under the fabric. Then she quickly looked up again. She must not look at his legs. She must not even think about his legs, nor any other body part. Not the arms that had held her, not the chest that she had pressed herself against, and not his lips. Definitely not his lips. She did not want to think of them most of all.

But how was she supposed to stop her mind from thinking of such things when they were so close it would be easy to reach out and take hold of his hands? Hands that were clenched together between his knees—clenched so tightly that the whiteness of his knuckles was showing.

Oh, yes, it would be easy to touch him. Easy and yet an impossibility.

Throughout the performance Rosie hardly heard a word the actors said, and nor could she follow the plot—which seemed far too complex for a simple musical comedy. Even when Lillie Langtry came on stage, to the accompaniment of rapturous applause and cheers, it seemed to pass her by in a blur. All she could think about was the silent man sitting beside her.

Like her, he sat ramrod-straight in his chair, as if attending a solemn funeral service, not a light-hearted comedy. When the audience laughed, he remained rigid. When they clapped enthusiastically at the end of each scene he gave a brief token applause.

To say he was not enjoying the play would be an understatement. He was obviously hating every minute of the performance. And she knew that was not the fault of the actors, the band, the writer or the director. There was only one person responsible for Alexander's bad mood. And that was her.

After an interminably long time the intermission arrived. At least this ordeal was halfway over. But that was of small comfort. With the lights now raised Rosie could no longer hide behind the darkness of the blackened auditorium. No longer could she pretend to be distracted by the performance.

She might have to make conversation with Alexander.

The prospect caused her already thumping heart to increase its tempo, and her skin to burn as if the theatre had suddenly turned into an inferno.

Charlotte and Arabella stood up and rushed out, saying something about getting refreshments.

Rosie sent a pleading look towards the door they had so hastily departed through, silently begging them to return and save her from this intolerable situation. But the door remained firmly shut. The girls did not return.

She turned to stare straight ahead. They were now alone. All alone except for Aunt Prudence, who seemed to have dozed off at some time during the performance.

Alexander also stared ahead, his body still rigid, his face implacable.

With her heart beating to a frantic rhythm and her breath coming in short, shallow gasps, Rosie scrambled for something to say. Anything to break this uncomfortable silence. But nothing came to her befuddled mind.

'Are you enjoying the play, Your Grace?' she finally asked, her voice barely audible.

'Yes,' was his terse reply.

They slipped back into silence.

'And did you have a good trip up from London?'

He exhaled loudly. 'Oh, for goodness' sake, Miss Smith. After all that has happened between us are we *really* going to indulge in meaningless polite conversation?'

Rosie bit her lip. Even thinking of polite conversation had required the concerted effort of all her mental capabilities. How was she supposed to think of anything more interesting to say when her mind was completely distracted by the close proximity of the man sitting beside her? A man who had once kissed her, had once told her he loved her, had even said that he wanted to marry her.

Rosie swallowed to ease her dry throat and tried not to think such things. She was supposed to make interesting conversation, not polite chatter. She most certainly did not want to say anything that would allude to what had happened between them at Knightsbrook. But what could she say?

She took a quick glance at Alexander, who was staring straight ahead. He wasn't much help. It was obvious he had no intention of making any conversation at all. At least she was trying—and all she had got for her trouble was a reprimand.

'Well, if you prefer we can sit here in embarrassed silence, staring at the walls and pretending we're somewhere else.'

He breathed in deeply and exhaled slowly. 'Forgive me—that was rude of me.'

Rosie shook her head. She did not want to argue with him. 'No, you have no need to apologise. This is awkward for both of us. I'm sure Arabella and Charlotte meant well, but I more than anyone should know that sometimes you should not interfere with people's lives.'

'Hmm…' came his monosyllabic reply.

Once again they sank into silence.

Alexander crossed his legs, uncrossed them,

then crossed them again. Arabella wondered if he too was struggling to think of something to say. She wished that in his agitation he would remain still. All his crossing and uncrossing was once again drawing her attention to his legs—and all the other parts of that magnificent body she was not going to think about.

Rosie swallowed again, her throat still stubbornly dry, and joined him in staring straight ahead.

'So Miss van Haven knew what you had done, I take it? She was in complete agreement with you pretending to be her?' he finally asked, breaking the protracted silence.

'Oh, yes,' Rosie nodded. 'It was a silly plan, I know. But Arabella—the real Arabella—didn't want to go to Knightsbrook because she didn't want to marry you, and she especially didn't want to go that weekend. She wanted to see the opening of Oscar Wilde's new play. So I came up with the plan, which she agreed to. If I pretended to be her and misbehaved terribly then you wouldn't want to marry her—or me, I mean.'

'You're right. It *was* a silly plan. But it looks like you succeeded.'

Rosie closed her eyes, his words like a stab to her heart. Yes, she had succeeded. Succeeded in saving Arabella from an unwanted marriage and succeeded in destroying her own chance of happiness with the man with whom she had fallen in love. But then, had Rosie Smith—the real Rosie Smith—ever had a chance of marrying the Duke or had she deluded herself?

'Well, that's something, I suppose,' she murmured, before they sank back into a tense silence.

Charlotte and Arabella bustled back in, their cheeks pink with excitement, matching smiles on their lips, and the curtain was raised for the second act.

Rosie could not be angry with her friend, nor with Charlotte. The two women had meant well, but they were trying to achieve a hopeless goal. Alexander despised her. That was undeniably evident to her, if not to them. He had made his feelings about her perfectly clear before she'd left Knightsbrook, and he was making them clear now. And even if he didn't despise her, the best she could hope for from Alexander was indifference. He was a duke and she was a nobody—a nobody he could now hardly bear even to speak to.

Once again she returned to staring at the stage, seeing nothing and hearing nothing of the performance, and waited anxiously for the whole embarrassing episode to be over.

Alexander had never felt like a victim before. But, sitting in The Gaiety Theatre, it seemed to him that was exactly what he was. The unwitting victim of a female conspiracy.

He had no doubt that this ridiculous situation was all down to Charlotte and Miss van Haven's scheming. While they had both looked as pleased as Punch when he and Charlotte had entered the box, Miss Smith had looked as shocked as he had felt. Her stilted conversation and awkward demeanour had made it abundantly clear that she would rather be anywhere than confined in this small theatre box watching this seemingly endless play.

He had never expected to see Rosie again. Had hoped he would never see her again. Now, with her sitting next to him, so close he could easily take her in his arms, everything about their weekend together came crashing over him, like a furious wave smashing against a rocky coastline.

The scent of spring flowers filled the air and the soft skin of her naked arms and shoulders seem to offer an all but irresistible temptation. An image of folding down the delicate straps of her gown and kissing a line along the skin of those slim shoulders invaded his mind.

He coughed discreetly and crossed his legs.

Yes, he really was a victim. A victim of Charlotte and Arabella's scheming and a victim of his own foolish desires. And he was going to have to fight those desires with the full might of his strength if he was to maintain his resistance and stop this woman from once again tearing out his heart.

She had hurt him. There was no denying that. And only a masochist would subject himself to continued pain. He was no masochist. As soon as this play was over he would leave, and then he would never have to experience the turmoil of such unwanted emotions ever again.

Finally the play finished, and the sound of hundreds of gloved hands applauding erupted in the theatre. Charlotte and Arabella instantly started chatting enthusiastically about everything they had just seen, while Rosie and Alexander maintained their now familiar uncomfortable silence.

'Right,' said Miss van Haven, standing up and picking up her shawl. 'We're staying at the Savoy and I've booked a table in the restaurant for supper. It will be my treat. It's the least I can do for you, Your Grace and Lady Charlotte, after the appalling trick I played on you.'

Alexander quickly stood up too. 'Not at all, Miss van Haven. You owe us nothing, and Charlotte and I would not dream of imposing.'

'Oh, please, Alexander,' Charlotte entreated him. 'I've never been to the Savoy and I'd love to see it. I'm sure you would as well. It's got electric lighting, you know, and a wonderfully modern contraption called a lift car that carries you up from one floor to another and then back down again.'

She stared at him, wide-eyed, as if the thought of seeing modern innovations should be enough to counter his severe reluctance to spend any more time in the company of Rosie Smith.

'That's as may be, Charlotte, but—'

'Oh, please, Alexander,' Charlotte said again, her eyes pleading. 'We don't get up to London often, and who knows when we'll come again? I would enjoy it so much.'

'Oh, all right, Charlotte. Fine,' he agreed through clenched teeth, sending her a silent message that they would not be staying long.

Charlotte clapped her hands together and beamed at him. It was obvious that it wasn't the thought of supper at the Savoy or of being able to travel by an electric lift from floor to floor that was causing so much excitement, but the fact that she had succeeded in forcing him to endure even more time with Miss Smith.

He escorted the ladies out through the noisy milling crowd and hailed a cab to take them to the Savoy.

As they travelled towards the well-known London landmark Alexander had to admit that Charlotte was right to be enthusiastic about the way the Savoy had embraced modernity. Like a beacon, it shone out in the London night sky, with electric lighting illuminating every room. The carriage pulled up into the courtyard and he helped the ladies down.

Rosie waited till last, and seemed to take a moment to compose herself before she took his offered hand. She placed one foot on the carriage steps and their eyes met.

Despite his attempted resistance to her charms, he had to admit he had never seen her look more beautiful. Her blue eyes sparkled with reflected light, capturing his gaze, and he stood in front of her as if transfixed.

It wasn't until she lowered her eyes and a blush came to her creamy cheeks that he remembered himself. He took her hand in his and forced himself to recall who she was and what she had done. Even with her gloved hand in his he would not lose his composure—he would not react to the light touch of her fingers that was burning into his hand.

Her touch brought memories flooding back... of taking her in his arms and kissing her with such passionate intensity it had seemed to shake his world off its axis.

Do not think of that—and for goodness' sake, man, pull yourself together.

But even this admonition couldn't stop him from noticing that one tendril of black hair had become dislodged from her coiffure and now curled temptingly around her neck, across her shoulders and down to her beautiful cleavage...

They entered the restaurant and the head waiter ushered them to a table by the French doors, overlooking the balcony and garden.

'Would you like to see the electric lift?' Arabella said to Charlotte, ignoring the waiters who were holding out their chairs.

Before anyone else could respond the two girls had rushed off, leaving Alexander, Rosie and their elderly chaperon standing at the table.

They seated themselves in the plush red leather chairs and a bottle of champagne arrived, unordered. It seemed Miss van Haven's arrangements extended beyond merely getting Alexander and Rosie together. She wanted to make this a celebration as well. But this evening had more in common with a wake than it did a festive occasion.

Alexander made polite conversation with Miss van Haven's elderly aunt, who suddenly announced that all the excitement of the evening had brought on one of her headaches and decided to retire for the evening.

It was a complaint Alexander could have made himself. The tension of the evening was starting to leave its mark on him, in the form of tight shoulders and a stiff neck.

He offered to escort the aunt to her suite, but she waved him away with her fan and bustled off towards the stairs. It seemed that the elderly aunt, like his mother, abhorred modern apparatus such as electric lifts and would prefer to walk up to her room.

He lifted the champagne out of the ice bucket and poured it into two glasses.

'Champagne? Although I'm not entirely sure what we're meant to be celebrating. Perhaps we're supposed to offer up a toast to my sister for discovering the devious side of her personality?'

He handed a champagne flute to Rosie.

'I'm equally surprised by Arabella putting this plan into action,' she said, taking the champagne glass from his hand but carefully avoiding touching his fingers. 'I knew she had received a lot of letters lately that had made her very happy. I'd assumed they were from the theatre she's about to perform with, but they must have been from Charlotte.'

'Hmm… So you and Miss van Haven in the habit of concocting devious plans?'

She screwed up her pretty face and her shoulders rose up to her ears. 'Yes, I'm afraid we are. But I've learnt my lesson—even if Arabella hasn't.'

'She thought she'd be helping you by getting us together, and you thought you'd be helping her by passing yourself off as a badly behaved American heiress?'

She shrugged again. 'I suppose so…yes.'

He considered her for a moment as she blushed under his gaze. 'So the only reason you did it was to help your friend?'

'Well, no, that wasn't the only reason.' She bit her bottom lip. 'I also wanted to have some fun at the expense of a group of stuffy aristocrats. I thought you were just greedy people who didn't want to work for your money… I thought you deserved to be made sport of. I was wrong and I'm sorry. I know now that I shouldn't have. I shouldn't really make fun of anyone.'

Alexander looked down into his glass at the bubbles rising up through the straw-coloured liquid and bursting when they hit the surface as he absorbed this piece of information.

'Perhaps… But your main reason was to help your friend. You had honourable intentions, even if you were misguided,' he said.

He looked over at her. Despite his conciliatory words her blush had not subsided.

'You're very kind to say that,' she mumbled. 'But I still shouldn't have done it and I beg your pardon.'

He shook his head. 'No, it seems you have nothing to apologise for. You were helping a friend. I jumped to the conclusion that you were up to no good—that you were playing games with me or performing some sort of confidence trick on my family. I judged you unfairly. I should have known there would be a reason for your behaviour and I didn't give you a chance to explain. For that I am sorry.'

Alexander suspected his reaction had also been influenced by his history with Lydia Beaufort. He had been lied to before, cheated before, tricked before, and that had coloured his assessment of Rosie Smith. But Rosie was not like Lydia. Lydia had lied to achieve her own disreputable ends—not to help a friend.

'No, no, no.' Rosie shook her head emphatically. 'You most definitely have nothing to apologise for. My behaviour was terrible—and not in the way it was meant to be terrible. When I came up with my plan I didn't think about the people I would be deceiving. I just wanted to save Arabella and have some fun in the process. It really was quite appalling.'

'No, Miss Smith. I should be the one to apologise. I said some awful things to you. I was rude and offensive, and you did not deserve that.'

Alexander cringed as memory came flooding back—all those accusations he had made, all those harsh words he had said. It really had been unforgivable—especially now that he knew she had not been lying to him for her own sake, but to help her friend.

She held up her hands to stop his words. 'You

were angry. And you had every right to be after the way I acted. I came into your home, I was rude to your mother, I tricked you and Charlotte. It was disrespectful. You said when we first met that everyone deserves to be treated with respect. You most certainly do—as does Charlotte, and even your mother…' She gave a little laugh. 'Well, perhaps your mother deserves to have tricks played on her…' She pulled her face into a more serious expression. 'No, even dowager duchesses deserve to be treated with respect.'

It was lovely to see that smile again—that beautiful, radiant smile—even if it was only for a fleeting moment. Alexander took a moment to bask in its remembered glow before asking a question that had been tormenting him since he had found out she was not really Arabella van Haven.

'And what of Thomas Gardener. Was he in on this game?'

She bit the edge of her bottom lip again. 'Oh, him. Yes, about him… I…um… I sort of…well, I made him up.'

He stared at her as she sent him a tentative smile. 'So there is no Thomas Gardener?'

She shook her head.

'Why on earth did you invent him? What did *he* have to do with your plan?'

Her flushed cheeks coloured a darker shade

of pink. 'Well, you put me on the spot when you asked why I didn't want to marry. I couldn't think of any reason why I wouldn't want to marry a man like—' She bit that poor lip again. 'I couldn't think of any reason why I wouldn't want to get married, so I invented a beau. I named him Thomas after a sleeping ginger tomcat, and Gardener after an elderly man pushing a wheelbarrow.'

He stared at her in disbelief as she smiled through her embarrassment, and then laughter exploded within him. He had tormented himself with jealousy over a cat and his aging gardener.

'Oh, Rosie, you really are—' He stopped suddenly, his laughter dying. 'I'm sorry. Miss Smith.'

Her smile grew wider. 'Oh, no, call me Rosie, please. It is my real name, after all. And I'm so sorry I lied about having a beau.'

'As I've said, you have nothing to apologise for. Now that I know the full story it seems it is only I who needs to apologise. I should have given you a chance to explain. I should not have jumped to conclusions. You say you have behaved terribly, but you were doing so for honourable reasons. I have no such excuse for my own unreasonable behaviour.'

She sent him a small smile. 'Oh, well…perhaps we should just agree that we're both really terrible people?'

Alexander laughed again. 'Yes, we're terrible people who deserve each other!'

He placed his hand over hers, and then, suddenly realising the easy level of informality he had slipped into, removed it, picked up his champagne and drained the glass.

'So, perhaps you'd like to tell me about the real Rosie Smith.' He placed the now empty glass back on the table. 'I know she plays the piano exquisitely, that she loves nature and that art enraptures her. I know she's funny, and that she is a good and loyal friend to Miss van Haven. But what else can you tell me about the real Rosie Smith?

She shrugged. 'There's not much to tell, really. As I already told you, I'm Mr van Haven's ward. I have been since I was fourteen.'

That familiar sadness washed over her deep blue eyes. It had intrigued him from the first time he had seen her. A sadness so at odds with her ready smile and easy laughter.

'But I once did have my own family.' She smiled as if lost in her memories. 'My father was an electrical engineer, and he ran a successful company installing electricity in towns and businesses throughout New York State. Mr van Haven convinced him to expand, but unfortunately it didn't work out. He lost money on bad debts and other misfortunes. He couldn't repay the money he owed to Mr van Haven's bank, so the bank took over his company. Not long after that he died. I think he died of a broken heart. He was certainly a broken man. Mr van Haven then employed my mother as a governess for Arabella. I don't know if that was an act of charity, guilt because of what he had done to my father, or because he knew my talented and accomplished mother would make the perfect governess and substitute mother for Arabella. And, being a cunning businessman, he knew she was desperate to find work and a place to live—somewhere she could keep her child with her. That meant she wouldn't object to the low wages he paid. My mother died when I was fourteen, but thanks to Arabella Mr van Haven took me on as his ward. That's why I owe so much to Arabella; she's the best friend a girl could ever have.'

Alexander could now see why such sadness clouded her otherwise sunny disposition. She had lost her father and her mother at an early age— had gone from a secure family life to one of insecurity, dependent on a man who seemed to have little regard for other people. He could also see why she was such a resilient young woman. She'd had to be, if she was to survive under such conditions.

He had been right in his original assessment: she really was a remarkable young woman.

'I'm sorry, Rosie. That must have been very hard for you,' he said, gently patting her hand.

She sent him a sad smile. 'It was. But I always had Bella.'

'I can see you two are very close.'

She nodded and they slipped into silence, both staring into their glasses.

Her life had been so hard, he thought, and yet she continued to smile and laugh, even through her sorrow. She was clever, witty, loyal and so beautiful it could take his breath away. How could he ever have doubted her? And why had he wasted so much time and so much energy feeling pain and anger towards her? It had to be due to what had happened between him and Lydia Beaufort.

But Lydia was in his past. Rosie was here, now, and very much part of his present. And the two women couldn't be more different.

He looked up at her and smiled. 'Your father was an electrical engineer?'

Rosie beamed a smile back at him. 'Yes, I'm sure you two would have got on well. He would have loved your plans for modernisation and would have had many ideas to contribute.'

'And he also produced a rather lovely, rather clever and innovative daughter as well,' he said, causing that delightful blush to tinge her creamy cheeks once again. 'I would have been honoured to meet him. It's men like your father who will transform this country. Not the old aristocracy who are still clinging on to their old ways, desperate to preserve a class system that is rapidly becoming outdated.'

She looked at him sideways, no longer smiling. 'Don't let your mother hear you say that. She thinks a title means everything, and that finding you a woman from a wealthy family who thinks the same way will save Knightsbrook.'

Alexander exhaled loudly. 'My mother knows exactly what I think of that. I've told her often enough. I don't care about my title and I care even less about other people's titles. The estate I have inherited means more than the title. What I have inherited is the responsibility of running it well, and improving it—not just for my family, but for everyone who depends on the estate for their livelihood. My mother and many like her think a title gives you privileges, but the title of Duke and Duchess should go to people who take their responsibility seriously.'

'Really?' Rosie gave him another sideways glance. 'You don't care about titles, class, background...? All that sort of thing?'

'There are more important things—like character, personality, resilience.'

He was about to add other frivolous attributes, such as beauty, a ready laugh and a lovely smile, when he was interrupted by the two co-conspirators, returning arm in arm.

Alexander suspected they had been hiding just out of sight and watching all that had unfolded between him and Rosie, waiting until their differences had been resolved before they made their reappearance.

Over the meal they discussed the play—although Alexander could contribute little, having seen virtually nothing of it, his mind having been occupied elsewhere. They also talked of what the girls had seen in London, and Arabella's ambitions as an actress. Uncharacteristically, Rosie did not say much, but she smiled a lot, particularly when she looked at Alexander, and that warmed his heart.

The crowd at the Savoy Restaurant began to thin, until they were the only people remaining at their table. Alexander had so thoroughly enjoyed the company of these young women, and the pleasure of once again being comfortable in Rosie's company, he had failed to notice how late it was getting.

He looked over at the waiters, who were not too successfully stifling yawns, and reluctantly decided it was time to call it a night. But he knew it would not be the last time he would see Rosie Smith. They had a lot of time to make up—time they had wasted in foolish misunderstandings and unnecessary pain and anguish.

Arabella was the first to stand, and she asked Charlotte to accompany her to her suite. 'It will give you one more chance to play on the electric lift,' she said. And the two girls rushed off together, leaving Alexander and Rosie alone to say their goodbyes.

Alexander stood and held out his hand to Rosie. With a shy smile she placed her hand lightly on his and stood. They gazed at each other for a moment.

'It has been lovely to see you again,' he said, knowing his words were inadequate to express what he was feeling.

'And you too, Alexander.'

Charlotte was suddenly at his side, still beaming the smile that had not left her lips all evening. Rosie kissed Charlotte on the cheek and thanked her for everything she had done, before sending Alexander another smile and departing.

As Charlotte and Alexander waited for their hansom cab to take them back to their townhouse, curiosity got the better of him.

'I have to ask you,' he said. 'How did you manage to organise all this?'

Charlotte gave a little laugh. 'Oh, it was surprisingly easy. I wrote to the newspaper that reviewed the Oscar Wilde play—the one that mentioned Arabella van Haven. I asked them to forward a letter on to her. They did. She wrote back and explained what Rosie had done, and why. I knew there was no point just telling you— you'd never listen…'

Alexander had to nod his agreement. He was so stubborn he had refused to listen to Rosie when she had tried to explain herself by the river, and he would no doubt have refused to listen to Charlotte. He had been so caught up in his own anguish he had become completely unreasonable.

'Arabella and I decided the best thing to do was to get you two together so you could talk it out yourselves. So we did. And it seems we were right.'

Alexander smiled at his sister. Normally he would be annoyed with anyone trying to interfere in his life—after all, didn't he get enough of that from his mother? But this time, he had to admit, a little interference had been a great success.

Chapter Twenty-One

Alexander stared at his reflection as his valet brushed down his jacket, removing every last speck of dust so it was immaculately clean. Although such meticulous attention to detail was wasted. He would be returning by train to Knightsbrook this morning, and no doubt when he arrived he would be speckled with the smuts emitted from the steam train's funnel.

He hadn't wanted to come to London—had not wanted to waste time on such frivolity. It was only Charlotte's insistence that had dragged him away from his work. He had been annoyed by the interruption, but now he couldn't be more grateful to Charlotte for insisting he accompany her to the theatre.

She had also been right that he'd needed to find out why Rosie had deceived him. He had tried to convince himself that it didn't matter, but in reality he had been tormenting himself with unanswered questions. Possible reasons to explain why someone who had seemed so lovely could behave so treacherously had been spinning round and round in his head.

And now he knew the answer. She was not treacherous, and she was not deceitful. She was an honourable, lovely and lively young woman.

He smiled to himself at the memory of how she had looked as they'd dined at the Savoy. Then further images entered his mind. Her twirling her way down the entrance hall at Knightsbrook... her talking and laughing with Annie...her playing the piano with such passion and virtuosity.

Yes, he owed a debt of gratitude to Charlotte for tricking him and overcoming his stubborn resistance to meeting Rosie again.

He thanked his valet, picked up his hat and gloves and headed downstairs. Charlotte was waiting for him, her trunk and hat box stacked by the front door, ready for their departure.

They were going home—back to Knightsbrook. Away from London...away from Rosie. Alexander knew he must pen a letter to her immediately, before they left town. He had to inform her of how much he had enjoyed their reunion and how much he was looking forward to seeing them again.

He called for some pen and paper.

Or, better than a quick farewell note, perhaps

he should extend an invitation to Rosie, Arabella and Aunt Prudence to spend some time at Knightsbrook. That would provide an opportunity to re-do their time together—this time with no pretence, no artifice, and no barriers put in place by him.

The pen and paper arrived and he dipped the pen in the ink, watched over by a very interested Charlotte. He put the pen to the paper, then hesitated.

'What's wrong, Alexander?' Charlotte asked, her brow furrowed.

'I've changed my mind.'

The furrow grew deeper.

'I believe we deserve a longer break in London. Perhaps we should invite Miss Smith and Miss van Haven to accompany us on a drive around Hyde Park? I'm sure the air would do us all some good.'

Charlotte's furrowed brow smoothed. She clapped her hands together and smiled. 'That's a marvellous idea, Alexander.' Then her smile disappeared and she placed the back of her hand theatrically on her brow. 'Oh, but I think you might have to go by yourself… I can feel a terrible headache coming on.'

Alexander shook his head and smiled at his sister. 'If that's your best performance, then I don't think you should consider a career on the stage.

And you don't need to feign a headache. I'm sure Miss Smith and Miss van Haven would be delighted to see you again.'

'Well, perhaps—but I can see them another time. I hope there will be many more times we will all spend together. So, off you go.'

Alexander grabbed his hat and gloves and hailed a hansom cab to take him to the Savoy. There, standing at the reception desk, he penned a note to the Misses Smith and van Haven, inviting them and their chaperon for a drive in Hyde Park.

As he waited for their reply he paced up and down the foyer, feeling ridiculously nervous, like a young man waiting for his beau.

He heard the clanking of the electric lift behind him, turned and saw Rosie emerging. Dressed in a dark blue skirt, with a blue and white striped blouse, she looked a vision. Could she have become even more beautiful overnight? Was that even possible? He could have sworn it was a fact. And she was smiling at him—that radiant smile that seemed to light up the room.

'Alexander,' she said when she reached him, still beaming that smile.

He nodded a greeting, unable to stop himself from smiling his own foolish smile.

She looked back at the stairs. 'I'm afraid we're going to have to wait for Aunt Prudence. She refuses to take the electric lift as she says it is a new-fangled contraption.' Rosie bit the top of her lip, as if suppressing a giggle. 'And Arabella says she can't join us because she has a headache.'

Alexander laughed. 'There seems to be a lot of that going around. Charlotte, too, seems to have been struck down suddenly by a mysterious headache.'

Aunt Prudence joined them, and Alexander took both ladies' arms and led them to a waiting carriage.

The carriage took them through the grand entrance to Hyde Park, where they joined the parade of locals exercising their horses and riding in carriages along the path, under the canopy of lightly rustling trees.

'Oh, let's walk, Alexander!' Rosie said, patting his arm. 'You know how much I love trees and nature.'

Alexander laughed, but told the driver to stop. 'From memory, I think you said trees were horrid and those terrible birds were even worse.'

Smiling, Rosie patted him on the arm again. 'I never said that. That was Arabella.'

He helped the two ladies down from the carriage and took each one by the arm. They walked in silence for a few moments, before Aunt Prudence released his arm and headed for the nearest bench.

'You two young people go ahead. I can feel another one of my headaches coming on.'

Alexander rushed to the older woman's side. 'Shall I summon the carriage?'

'No, no. I'll just sit here under the trees until I start to feel better. You two young people carry on with your walk.'

Rosie sent him a small wink.

'Did you know that would happen?' Alexander asked.

'You can almost set your clock by Aunt Prudence's headaches, so I knew if we decided to walk it wouldn't be long before she claimed another imaginary headache and then we'd be able to spend some time together.'

He laughed as she raised her eyebrows and tried to look innocent. 'You really are quite devious, aren't you?'

'I thought you would have realised that by now, Alexander,' she said, and laughed as she took his arm.

They strolled along the path together. Alexander was suddenly strangely tongue-tied—unsure what to say now that all barriers between them had been lowered.

'I hope you enjoyed last night's play,' he said, to break the silence.

'Oh, yes, it was marvellous,' she responded, and then gave one of her now familiar tinkling laughs. 'No, I'm sorry, Alexander. That's not true. I can hardly remember any of the play. I wasn't concentrating. I was so distracted by seeing you again.'

He had to smile at her response, which was so unguarded. 'I was the same, I'm afraid. But apparently it has had good reviews, so it seems we missed an excellent play.'

'Well, we might have missed an excellent play, but I for one think it was still a great night.'

He squeezed her arm lightly in agreement.

Their walk took them past a pond, where groups of young boys were playing with boats on the water. The miniature flotilla included vessels of all sizes, from simple boats of sticks and cloth to elaborately carved sailing vessels.

'Shall we stop and watch for a while?' Rosie asked.

'I'm so pleased we talked last night,' he said as he led her to a nearby park bench. 'I feel we now have a chance to start all over again, and for me to get to know the real Rosie Smith.'

'Oh, I'm afraid the person you've already met is mostly Rosie Smith. I might have been lying about my name, but almost everything else about the person you met at Knightsbrook was the real me.'

She tucked her skirt underneath her and sat down.

'Sadly, the person who twirled down the entrance hall at Knightsbrook, and the person who sang inappropriate songs in the Dowager's drawing room, is the real Rosie Smith.'

Alexander smiled as he remembered her unusual entrance and the look of horror on his mother's face. 'I'm pleased to hear that.' He sat down beside her on the bench and looked out at the busy children. 'And I wouldn't have it any other way. Your twirling entrance was priceless.'

She patted his arm again and smiled. 'That wasn't my intention. I was supposed to be shocking you, not impressing you. You were supposed to conclude that I was entirely unacceptable.'

'I don't think it would be possible for me to think that the real Rosie Smith is unacceptable.'

She sent him a shy smile and a delightful blush tinged her cheeks.

'And I was the one whose behaviour was unacceptable. You said you expected to meet a stuffy aristocratic family, and after my reaction that must have been exactly what you thought of me. A delightful young woman had come into my home, bringing laughter and joy, and I reacted by being disapproving and stern.'

'Oh, no—no.' She turned to him, shaking her head, with a deep furrow in her brow. 'You are most definitely not stuffy, and you were nothing but polite. I mean, the first time we met you saved me from falling to the ground.'

Alexander smiled again at the memory of Rosie, diving across the room to save the Ming vase. It was strange, but even then he had been more concerned for her welfare than for an irreplaceable valuable vase.

'And if you were sombre at times—well, you had reason to be,' she said in a quieter voice. 'You've had all those problems with your father, with the estate, and then there's Lydia...'

Lydia. The name caused no reaction in Alexander whatsoever. It was as if some kind of an exorcism had been performed and her spirit no longer haunted him. 'The only problem with Lydia is that she caused me to judge you more harshly than you deserved.'

Memories of what Charlotte had said came back to him—that because of Lydia he had hardened his heart, had shut down emotionally. And yet when he had met Rosie she had managed to find a chink in his armour and he'd begun to open himself up to her. That was why her perceived betrayal had hurt him so much. But now he knew she had not betrayed him. He had been given a second chance.

He smiled at her, and got a beautiful smile in return. 'As for the estate—I've secured sufficient advances from the bank to begin a modernisation programme, and what convinced the bank manager the most was my telling him of your suggestion to diversify and bring electrification to the dairy and the woolshed. He was most impressed with my progressive thinking.'

'*Whose* progressive thinking?' she said, raising her finger and waggling it in front of his face.

'*Your* progressive thinking!' He laughed, taking her finger and giving it a light kiss. 'And for that I thank you—on behalf of my family and all the tenants of Knightsbrook.'

He continued holding her soft hand for a moment, before reluctantly releasing it.

'I'm so pleased, Alexander,' she said quietly. 'I know how much Annie and the tenants mean to you. They're more than just people who work on your land, aren't they? They're family.'

He nodded. 'They are indeed. As a child I often used to pretend to myself that Annie was my real mother, her husband my real father, and the tenant children my brothers and sisters.'

She placed her hand gently on his arm and he smiled at her.

'At least that is something for me to be grateful to my father for,' he said, with a laugh that contained no humour. 'He taught me a valuable lesson: that there are good and bad people in all classes. It doesn't matter what your background is, who your family is, or how much money you have, it's what's in your heart that matters.'

She nodded her agreement.

'And that's something I admire in *you*, as well, Rosie.'

'Me?' she said, pointing to herself.

'You've risen above your circumstances. You might have become bitter or angry, but instead you smile more than some people who have had a good life handed to them on a silver platter.'

She shook her head in disagreement. 'In many ways I think my life has been much easier than a lot of people's. Before things changed I had a very happy childhood, and I have warm, lovely memories from that time. I had a mother and father who loved me, and a home that was full of laughter, joy and music. I think it was that start in life that gave me such resilience and allowed me to rise above misfortune. When my father lost all his money, and then died, it was heartbreaking. But I still had my lovely mother, who was a very strong woman. She tried to protect me as much as possible from what was happening. And when she became Arabella's governess she continued to be a loving mother to me and became a substitute mother for Arabella as well.'

She paused and took in a deep breath.

'When she died…yes, I was devastated, and I felt very frightened and alone. But I had my friend Arabella. We were united in our grief and we supported each other. That's why we're such good friends now.' She sent him a sad smile. 'So, yes,

I've had a lot of sadness in my life—but there's also been a lot of happiness and a lot of kindness.'

Alexander's admiration for this remarkable young woman continued to grow. She had been through so much, and yet there wasn't a hint of self-pity, a hint of anger against how unfairly the world had treated her.

'I've said it before but I'll say it again: you really are an impressive young woman.'

She raised her hands in protest. 'Well, perhaps it's as you said. Life teaches you lessons. Your father's behaviour taught you to value your tenants, and my misfortune taught me to appreciate my friendship with Arabella and all the good things in my life.' She tilted her head and gave another sad smile. 'And my time with you taught me the folly of playing silly games—they can backfire spectacularly.'

'Oh, no, Rosie, don't change a thing about yourself.'

They smiled at each other, then went back to watching the young boys at their carefree play.

'Oh, Aunt Prudence!' Rosie said suddenly, standing up. 'If my timings are correct she should be starting to feel slightly better and will by now feel that she is capable of the arduous journey home. That is as long as the driver doesn't go over any bumps and set off her imagined lumbago.'

They made their way back to the bench where

they had left Aunt Prudence, but as they approached Alexander could see they had no need to worry. She had engaged an elderly gentleman sitting at her bench in conversation.

'Well, well, well!' Rosie laughed. 'It looks like Aunt Prudence has found the cure for a headache. Perhaps we should patent it.'

Alexander bowed to the elderly gentleman and they made a round of introductions. While Rosie smiled on, Aunt Prudence blushed and simpered, almost like a young girl. And then the three of them made their way back to the park's entrance, where Alexander hailed a carriage to take them back to the Savoy.

He escorted them into the foyer and Aunt Prudence departed up the stairs. Alexander knew he had to say goodbye to Rosie, but he was reluctant for his time with her to come to an end.

'Lady Jennings is having a ball tonight, and Charlotte and I have been invited. I would be honoured if you, Miss van Haven and Aunt Prudence would join us.'

In fact Alexander had already declined the invitation, as had Charlotte, but he was sure Lady Jennings would have no objection. He rarely attended balls, and had no real interest in attending this one, but he did not want to leave London without seeing Rosie at least one more time. Having to dance and make small talk would be a very small price to pay for one more evening in her company.

She smiled her delightful smile and bobbed a little curtsey. 'Why, Your Grace, I would be honoured,' she said, with mock formality.

Chapter Twenty-Two

The ballroom glittered with reflected candlelight and couples glided round the highly polished parquet dance floor, the women in an array of colourful gowns, and the sound of music filling the air.

Rosie and Arabella paused at the entrance and Rosie took a moment to compose herself. Her heart was beating so hard it was almost drowning out the sound of the music, and her nerves were tingling at the thought of meeting Alexander again.

Their day together in the park had been so special. And now she was going to spend the evening dancing with that wonderful man.

She took in a deep breath and looked around the room. Then she she saw him, standing on the far side of the room, staring straight at her. She gasped in another breath as once again the image of a Greek statue entered her mind. She swallowed. And this Greek statue was walking straight towards her, his dark eyes fixed firmly on hers.

He reached the group and bowed his greetings to Arabella and Aunt Prudence, and then, taking Rosie's hand he formally asked her to dance.

Her heart hammering in her chest, Rosie could only nod her agreement and hope she wouldn't betray her nerves by tripping over the hem of her pink gauze gown or trampling his leather-booted feet.

He took her in his arms and they joined the couples circling the room in a waltz. It was the first time she had been in Alexander's arms since he had kissed her. And now he was dancing with Rosie Smith, a poor orphan, not with the woman he assumed was an American heiress. And he was doing it in front of everyone.

Rosie doubted it was possible to feel happier.

His hand held her waist firmly as he led her round the floor. She suspected the gap that was supposed to be maintained between dancing couples at all times was narrowing scandalously. But Rosie cared not a bit whether anyone was scandalised. All she wanted was to be even closer to this magnificent man. For his arms to be encircling her, for his lips to be kissing hers.

She sighed deeply and moved in even closer, tempted to place her head on his broad shoulder.

The dance ended and he led her off the dance

floor. Rosie could see outraged faces looking in their direction, and hear muttered voices. Everyone was wondering who this nobody was that she had captured the attentions of His Grace the Duke of Knightsbrook.

Usually such a reaction would have got Rosie's hackles up—would have caused her to poke out her tongue or do something else outrageous to shock them further. But tonight she was too happy to care how they looked at her or what they were saying about her.

Removing two glasses from the tray of a passing footman, Alexander handed one to Rosie. She was sure her face must be burning red—something she knew young ladies should avoid at all cost. But how could she stop her excitement from being reflected on her cheeks?

Alexander smiled at her—that wonderful smile that had once been so rare, but which she was now starting to see more often—and her cheeks burnt brighter.

'May I write my name on your dance card for the next dance?'

She handed him the card and the tiny pencil, then laughed as he wrote his name in bold letters diagonally across the card, claiming her for himself for the entire evening.

'Why, Your Grace, I don't believe that is entirely appropriate.'

His smile turned to a laugh. 'Why, Miss Smith, being in your company makes me want to behave entirely *inappropriately.*'

Rosie didn't think she could smile more brightly, but she did. 'I'm very pleased to hear it.'

'Shall we?' He offered her his arm to escort her back on to the dance floor for the quadrille.

They danced together throughout the night, only breaking apart when supper was announced, but Rosie knew she was far too excited to eat.

'Would you like to take some air?' Alexander asked, and Rosie nodded gratefully. 'With the doors open Aunt Prudence will be able to see us, so we won't further scandalise the guests.'

They looked over to where Aunt Prudence was seated, talking to the elderly gentleman she had met in the park. It was unlikely that the distracted chaperon would be keeping an eye on her charge, and that suited Rosie just fine.

With as much discretion as possible they left the ballroom for the balcony. She looked out over the dark garden, where the nearby flowering shrubs were lit up by the light cascading out of the ballroom.

Now that they were outside she was hoping the night air would cool her burning cheeks, but there was little chance of that. Not with Alexander standing so close she could feel the warmth

of his body and smell that wonderful masculine
scent of his.

He gently took hold of her hands and Rosie
made a small step closer to him.

'Rosie, thank you so much for coming tonight.
It's as if we've been given a chance to start again.'

Rosie sent him a quivering smile. Wild horses
wouldn't have stopped her from coming to tonight's ball and the chance of seeing him again.

She nodded her head slightly. 'It's been magical, Alexander,' she murmured.

He pulled her closer, into the shadows, and
Rosie eagerly moved with him. He leant down
and his lips lightly touched Rosie's. It was the
lightest of touches, but it set off a burning on her
lips that sparked through her body.

She reached up and put her hands around his
neck, wishing he would kiss her the way he had
when they were at Knightsbrook.

Her wish came true. He swept her into his
arms, holding her tightly. As if a dam had been
ruptured his kiss burst over her, swamping her
in its passionate embrace. She moulded herself
against his strong body as his kiss deepened. It
was as if he could not get enough of her, and she
knew she could not get enough of him.

Closing her eyes, she surrendered herself to the
sensation of his lips on hers, his arms surround-
ing her, his body pressed up against her. Her lips

parted wider as the hunger of his kiss intensified. She moaned with pleasure as his tongue entered her mouth, probing and tasting, filling her up, causing her to lose all sense of where she was. All she could do was give herself over to the powerful sensations rippling through her.

His hot, hungry lips kissed a line down her neck before returning once again to her demanding lips. She ran her hands through his thick hair, holding him closer, kissing him harder, loving the feel of his rough skin against her own soft cheeks, loving his masculine scent, loving the strength of his body. Loving *him*.

Music filled the air, as if in celebration of their kiss. And then Rosie realised she was being fanciful. The music signalled that the dancing had recommenced.

Slowly, Alexander broke from their kiss. 'Oh, Rosie. You are the most beautiful woman I have ever met,' he said, his voice cracking. He drew in a deep breath and looked towards the open doors. 'The dancing has recommenced. I believe we should return to the ballroom. We've already set tongues wagging, and our absence will be noted. If nothing else I wouldn't want to embarrass Aunt Prudence with our behaviour.'

Reluctantly, Rosie had to agree, and they reentered the ballroom.

For Rosie the rest of the evening went by in a

magical whirl of dancing and laughing. It really was a fairy tale come true, and she was the beautiful Cinderella on the arm of her handsome prince.

But when the evening came to an end she did not have to flee at midnight. Instead Alexander escorted her to the waiting carriage, which most definitely had not turned into a pumpkin.

He bowed formally, before helping her into the carriage. 'I'm afraid commitments are forcing me to return home tomorrow, but I would love you to visit Knightsbrook again soon.'

Rosie could hardly speak—could only nod, repeatedly.

'I will send a note with the arrangements. And of course Miss van Haven and Aunt Prudence are invited as well.'

Rosie raised her eyebrows. 'You aren't worried that your mother will try and matchmake you with Arabella?'

'In that case we will just have to invite Thomas Gardener as well,' he said, then laughed and kissed her hand.

Rosie's heart was singing as she rode home with Arabella and Aunt Prudence. He had invited the real Rosie Smith to Knightsbrook. He would be introducing her to his mother. Rosie knew this could only mean one thing: Alexander was officially courting her—Rosie Smith, a penniless orphan. It really was like a dream come true.

He had not yet declared his love for her, the way he had at Knightsbrook, and nor had he made any suggestion of marriage. But surely that was only a matter of time.

Oh, yes, it was almost too wonderful to believe.

But there was one thing Rosie did believe. Her excitement was so great she would not be sleeping that night.

Chapter Twenty-Three

Rosie was waiting anxiously for his letter to arrive. That had been her main occupation for the past week. With Arabella away at rehearsals she had little else to occupy her time. So she waited. And waited.

Apart from the wonderful affectionate note he had sent before he'd returned to Knightsbrook the day after the ball nothing had arrived from him, and it had been a whole week. A whole week of waiting.

The happiness that had filled her heart was ebbing away, to be replaced by increasing anxiety.

She paced backwards and forwards, up and down her hotel suite. Should she contact him? Would that be too forward? But what if something had happened to him? What if he was ill? Wouldn't he be expecting to hear from her? But if he wasn't ill, what would he think then? Should she just be content to wait until he contacted her? After all it had only been a week.

One whole week.

Once again she went down to the foyer, to ask the receptionist if there was any mail for her. This time surely there would be something waiting for her.

Making enquiries at Reception was something she did several times a day, even though she knew that if any letters did arrive they would be immediately sent up to her room.

As she approached the desk the receptionist shook his head sadly before she even had a chance to ask. She returned to her room, that fleeting bubble of optimism once again bursting, and leaving her deflated.

After being so loving and attentive, there had to be a good reason why he hadn't contacted her.

Rosie sat down at the desk and took out a piece of stationery. She was being silly. She should just write to him. A casual letter of enquiry about his health.

She wouldn't ask why he hadn't contacted her. She wouldn't ask why he hadn't written to her. And she would not mention that she was still waiting for her invitation to Knightsbrook. No, she wouldn't mention that. She would make sure her anxiety did not come through in any of the words she wrote.

And she most certainly would not accuse him of being remiss, of letting her down, causing her to go over and over their conversations, looking for something she might have said or not said that had given him offence. Something that might have caused him to change his mind and decide not to contact her again, as he had promised.

She dipped her pen in the ink pot and put it to the paper. Yes, she would write a casual, friendly letter, just enquiring after his health.

She stared at the blank page, her mind equally blank. Instead of writing she stood up and paced the room some more, wondering if any mail had arrived and whether she should take another trip down to the reception desk

A knock on the door sent her rushing across the room. It had arrived. The much-awaited letter had finally arrived.

She pulled open the door and clapped her hands together with glee when she saw a porter, bearing a silver tray containing the most valuable treasure Rosie could ever want. A crisp white envelope embossed with the Knightsbrook crest.

Rosie held it to her chest and sighed loudly. *Finally.* Finally he had contacted her. She savoured the moment and forced herself not to rip it apart to get to its contents. Instead she walked to the desk and picked up the silver letter opener, and with trembling hands slipped it under the edge of the envelope.

It was then that she saw the address. It wasn't for her. It was addressed to Arabella van Haven.

She stared at it. It had to be a mistake. Or was it a joke? Was Alexander playing a joke on her? Calling her Arabella instead of Rosie. That had to be it.

But until Arabella came home she would just have to wait and find out.

She placed the envelope on the desk, leaning it against the shelves, and stared at it.

She walked to the window and turned back to stare at the letter from across the room.

She looked over at the clock, ticking on the mantel. It would be another hour before Arabella was back from rehearsals. Could she hold out that long? Or would she succumb—do the unthinkable and open her friend's mail.

She walked over to the desk, picked up the letter, scanned both sides of it, then placed it down again. Picking up a book, she slumped down in an armchair, determined to divert herself as she waited for Arabella.

But her eyes kept leaving the book she wasn't reading and staring across the room at that letter.

After what seemed like the longest hour in Rosie's life Arabella returned. Before she had time to remove her hat and gloves—before she even had time to say hello—Rosie rushed across the room and grabbed the letter.

'There's some mail for you,' she said, thrusting the letter and the letter opener in Arabella's direction.

Arabella looked at Rosie's reflection in the mirror, one hand on her hat, the other removing a hatpin. She took off her hat and placed it on the sideboard, then took the letter from Rosie's outstretched hand and slit open the envelope while Rosie watched on anxiously.

Rosie waited, her anticipation mounting, as Arabella read the contents. Arabella placed her hand across her mouth. Not a good sign. She looked up at Rosie, her eyebrows pinched together, her mouth turned down in a frown, then back at the letter. Definitely not a good sign.

'What is it? Is Alexander ill? Is it worse?' *Oh, please God, do not let it be worse.*

'He's… He's…' Arabella handed her the card. 'I'm sorry, Rosie. I think you had better read it yourself.'

Rosie took the thick cream card and scanned the contents.

*The Dowager Duchess of Knightsbrook
has pleasure in inviting
Miss Arabella van Haven
to Knightsbrook on May the fifteenth, 1893,*

to celebrate the engagement of her son,
Alexander FitzRoy, Lord Ashton,
Eighth Duke of Knightsbrook,
to Elizabeth Barclay-Fortescue,
daughter of the Earl and Countess of Suffolk

Time seemed to stop. All sound seemed to evaporate except the pounding of Rosie's heart and the gasping of her breath.

There had to be a mistake.

She read the card again, then turned it over to see if there was anything on the back that would explain this absurdity. Nothing. She turned it over and read it one more time. There was no mistake. Alexander was engaged.

The card dropped from her hand and fluttered to the floor as her legs gave out from beneath her. She dropped to the floor, her voluminous skirts crumpling around her.

'Why would he do this? *Why?*' She looked up, appealing to Arabella, who looked down at her with an ashen white face.

'I am so sorry, Rosie. So very sorry.'

Rosie retrieved the card from the floor. 'Perhaps it was all a cruel game—a trick…a way of getting revenge on me? Perhaps that's what this has been all along. He wanted to hurt me the way I hurt him. He made me think that all was well between us so the shock would be even greater.'

She looked questioningly at Arabella. 'Could he be that cruel?'

She looked back down at the card. Rosie had not thought he would be capable of such a thing, but after everything that had happened she no longer knew what to believe.

'Or perhaps he's just succumbed to the reality of his financial situation. He needs money to save the estate, to protect everyone's livelihood. Perhaps he has decided that marrying an heiress is the most sensible, most responsible thing to do after all. And courting a penniless ward was never going to save Knightsbrook. But why didn't he tell me himself instead of letting me find out this way?'

She threw the card onto the floor.

'Oh, Rosie, I'm so sorry,' Arabella repeated, sitting down beside her and taking her in her arms. 'I should not have interfered. Now all I've done is made things worse for you, caused you even more heartache.'

The two friends sat together, holding each other, taking comfort in their friendship in a world that could sometimes be unfair.

Rosie rested her head on her friend's shoulder. 'No, Bella. This is not your fault. It's nobody's fault but mine—setting my sights on a duke, of all things. What was I *thinking*? Men like the Duke of Knightsbrook do not marry poor little orphans like Rosie Smith. They marry women like Elizabeth Barclay-Fortescue, daughter of the Earl and Countess of Suffolk.

'But Alexander did not seem like that to me,' Arabella said quietly.

'Nor to me either, Bella, but that is just the way of the world. I foolishly thought that after I'd explained everything to Alexander and he'd forgiven me we'd have some sort of future together. I'd forgotten one important fact. He's a duke and I'm a nobody. Well, I've remembered it now and I won't make that mistake again.'

'You're not a nobody, Rosie, and if he can't see how special you are then he's a fool.'

Rosie stood up and straightened her crumpled skirts. What was done was done and there was nothing she could do to change it. She knew she just had to get on with her life.

'Oh, well,' she said, with as much good humour as she could summon. 'I've already had practice in putting Alexander out of my thoughts. Now I have even more reason to forget him. He'll be more than out of my reach once he's married— he'll be completely unattainable. So the sooner I start not thinking about him the better.'

Arabella stood, picked up the discarded card, ripped it in two and sent Rosie a tentative smile. 'Yes. Just remember you're a survivor, Rosie.

You've survived a lot in the past and you'll survive this as well.'

Rosie smiled at her friend and blinked away her tears. She hoped Arabella was right, but at that moment she felt completely lost, and survival seemed far out of her grasp.

Chapter Twenty-Four

Alexander could hardly believe his mother's treachery. She had sunk to new depths in order to get her way. If he hadn't received a bill for one embossed invitation he would never have known what she was up to.

That she would have the audacity to send out a fake invitation to Arabella van Haven was beyond reprehensible. And then, when he confronted her, it had been to discover that she had been intercepting the mail and removing his letters to Rosie before the servants had had a chance to deliver them. That had left him speechless.

He had to put things right. Taking the train up to London and telling Rosie the truth was the only way. A letter would get there no faster, and he had to ensure that she understood the true situation.

Arriving at Paddington Station, he immediately jumped into a hansom cab and instructed the driver to get him to the Savoy as quickly as possible. He jumped from the cab almost before it had stopped, threw the fare in the driver's direction and ran into the foyer.

'I need to speak to Miss Rosie Smith,' he demanded of the receptionist.

The receptionist looked up from his ledger and shook his head. 'I'm afraid Miss Smith is not here. She left for the docks this morning. I ordered the carriage myself.'

The news hit Alexander like a punch to the stomach. She was leaving. She was going home. He was too late. His mother's plan had worked.

He turned and ran out of the foyer, hearing the receptionist calling out that he had left his hat behind. Running down the road towards the docks, he waved his arm wildly in the air to hail a cab.

Jumping in as soon as one stopped, he ordered the man to drive to the docks as fast as he could.

Unlike him, the driver knew which dock the steam ships departed from for America, and as they approached the Royal Albert Dock he could see a forest of sailing ships' masts and steamer chimneys.

A cacophony of sound hit him as he disembarked from the cab. Sailors of all nations were talking in a babble of foreign tongues, dock workers were yelling at each other as they loaded and unloaded cargo for the waiting vessels, chains clanked as large loads were hauled high in the air, wooden sailing ships creaked and the water lapped against the wooden beams of the docks.

Alexander looked in every direction, trying to see Rosie among the multitude of workers, passengers and merchants milling round the docks. Then he saw her, along with Aunt Prudence, standing beside a mound of trunks and suitcases. Her pretty face looked sad and she stared down at the ground, her usually upright posture slightly stooped.

He started running again. He had to stop her before she boarded the vessel that would take her away from him. He had to explain. He had to stop her leaving.

Reaching her, he came to a sudden stop, completely out of breath.

She looked up at him and gasped.

'Rosie, I…' He panted, trying to get his breath back. 'Rosie, I'm so sorry.'

He reached out his hand to her. She took a quick step back and clasped her hands tightly together, as if his touch was repugnant to her.

'Rosie, I'm sorry. Please let me explain.'

She shook her head and took another step backwards. 'There's nothing to explain. Nothing at all.'

She blinked several times and he could see tears in her eyes.

'Oh, and congratulations on your engagement.'

He stepped towards her. 'I'm not engaged, Rosie. That's what I want to tell you.'

She tilted her head. 'You're not… But I saw the engagement party invitation. It was sent to Arabella.'

He took in a few more breaths so he could speak more clearly. 'No. I am *not* engaged. My mother invented the whole thing. I don't think she expected me to find out, but she forgot that I do all the accounts, and the bill for one invitation was sent to me.'

'One invitation? But…' She shook her head in confusion.

'There was no engagement—no engagement party. Only one card was sent—to Arabella. She was obviously hoping that you'd return to America and we'd never see each other again. And it looks as if she almost succeeded.'

'So you're not engaged?' Rosie repeated, as if unable to comprehend this change of events.

'No, not yet.'

'Oh,' she said, lowering her head

'Not yet because you're going to have to marry me, Rosie. That's the only way I'm going to stop my mother from constantly interfering and matching me up with every passing heiress.'

Rosie's head shot up and her eyes grew wide. 'I'm going to have to *what*?' She gasped.

'Marry me, Rosie. I said you're going to have

to marry me. That's the only thing that will let my mother know that her interfering won't work.'

'What?' she repeated, her face a vision of confusion, and he realised what he had just said.

'I'm so sorry, Rosie. I've been running like a madman since I arrived in London, and in my haste that came out all wrong. Let me start again.'

He took in a few deep breaths to try and slow his racing thoughts so he could explain himself better.

'What I mean to say is that if we have a long courtship then it will give my mother too much opportunity to put obstacles in our way. She will be constantly trying to thwart our plans. Even when she fails—which she will—it will be a constant irritation, so I think we should marry as soon as possible.'

She stared back at him, her dazed eyes even wider.

'I'm still doing this wrong…' He dropped down onto one knee and took hold of Rosie's hand. 'Rosie Smith—my darling Rosie. I adore you. I love you. I think I've loved you from the moment I saw you twirling down the entrance hall at Knightsbrook House. I've never seen anyone so free, so full of joy, and I've never experienced such happiness as I do when I'm with you. Without you it's as if there is no daylight—only a long, interminable night. I can't offer you immediate wealth, but I can offer you a title, and my undying love and devotion, and one day I hope to be able to lavish you with all the luxuries that you deserve. Will you do me the honour…the very great honour…of consenting to be my wife?'

'Of course I will,' she said, nodding her head vigorously. 'And I don't want luxuries. I don't even want a title. All I want is you. All I've ever wanted is you.' She looked around at the bustling crowd and laughed. 'Now, get up, will you? People are staring at us, and you know how much I hate making a scene.'

He looked around and saw that she was right. Even among this crowd that had seen virtually everything before, they had caused the bustle to come to a halt and people to stare in their direction.

'Oh, I have a confession to make,' she said as he rose to his feet. 'I'm not departing. We're meeting Mr van Haven. This is his luggage. He and Arabella have gone off to get a carriage. Your mother sent him a telegram, telling him what had happened, and he got the next steam ship over here. Poor Arabella's probably getting a severe telling-off at the moment, and when he comes back he'll probably try and offer you a deal you can't resist so you'll make his daughter a duchess.'

They looked towards where the carriages were

waiting and saw Arabella and an older gentleman walking towards them.

'In that case we'll have to convince him that he's wasting his time,' said Alexander.

And with that he took his bride-to-be in his arms, lifted her off the ground and kissed her.

He knew that he had found his perfect duchess. A woman who would love him as deeply and passionately as he loved her, who would stand beside him and share his burdens the way he would stand beside her and share hers, and who would fill his days with love, laughter and happiness.

Epilogue

The wedding was to have been a simple affair:
just family, a few friends and the tenants. But Mr
van Haven had had other ideas. He was now connected to the aristocracy—albeit through a ward
he had never really wanted, and to whom he had
never paid more than the most minimal of attention—and he wanted to celebrate the fact. To that
end he had arranged a lavish affair, no expense
spared, and Rosie had conceded.

After being supported by Mr van Haven's reluctant charity for so many years, she had decided that letting him organise a large wedding at
Knightsbrook and allowing him to invite almost
every member of the British aristocracy was a
small price to pay.

A lavish wedding would also go some way
to appeasing the Dowager, who was still struggling to accept the fact that the next Duchess of

Knightsbrook came with no dowry. But now that her attention had turned to finding a good match for Charlotte, she was at least leaving Rosie and Alexander alone.

And she wasn't the only one desperately match-making. With so many dukes, earls, barons and viscounts assembled in one spot, Mr van Haven was like a child in a candy shop. The wedding was providing him with the ideal opportunity to thrust Arabella in front of as many aristocrats as he could. He still most definitely had ambitions in that direction.

Well, Mr van Haven was in for a big surprise. Marriage did not figure in Arabella's future. She would soon be appearing on the London stage— albeit in a minor role, with a production company that was struggling financially to survive—but Rosie was sure it was the first step in what would be a brilliant career.

Rosie could only hope that Mr van Haven's business concerns would take him back to America before Arabella's opening night. A career on the stage was certainly *not* the future Mr van Haven had envisaged for his only child.

At least Rosie would now be able to act as Arabella's chaperon. After all, what was more respectable than being chaperoned by a member of the aristocracy—a duchess, no less? Aunt Prudence would be able to return to America with

Mr van Haven, leaving the girls to enjoy themselves—and enjoy themselves is exactly what they were intending to do.

But they would think of that another day. Today they had a wedding to celebrate. *Her* wedding—something Rosie had never imagined would happen.

'Have I told you how radiant you look today, Rosie?' Arabella asked, joining her friend and linking arms.

'Only about a thousand times.'

'White lace definitely suits you. And it seems being a married woman also suits you. I've never seen you look happier or more beautiful.'

Smiling, Rosie hugged her best friend, who also looked radiant in a pale blue satin bridesmaid's gown.

It was hard to believe. She was now Rosie Ashton, the Duchess of Knightsbrook.

She looked over at her husband, who was in conversation with Annie, a delighted smile on his lovely lips. Alexander had insisted that all the tenants be invited to the wedding and the reception, much to his mother's and Mr van Haven's chagrin. But after much huffing and puffing they had been forced to accept his decision.

Alexander looked back at her. His smile grew larger and once again she was struck by how much he reminded her of a Greek statue—albeit one that now knew how to smile and laugh.

She smiled too, and a shiver of excited anticipation ran through her. Tonight she would finally discover whether he resembled a *naked* Greek athlete in all other respects.

He excused himself and walked towards her, causing her heart to beat faster. This handsome man, dressed in a dove-grey morning suit, his top hat long abandoned, was her husband. The man who had vowed to love and honour her until death did them part.

'I think I'll leave you two alone,' Arabella said with a light laugh. 'I'm sure my father has some man with a sizeable income and a country estate that he's dying to introduce me to.'

Alexander took Rosie's hands and lightly kissed her cheek. 'While the music, the dancing and the champagne are distracting everyone, there is something we really must do,' he whispered in her ear. 'Will you allow me to lure you away from our guests so I can satisfy a demanding urge that's starting to overwhelm me?'

Rosie nodded. Oh, yes, he could lure her away…and he could satisfy whatever urge he had.

He took her hand and led her across the grass, past the tables draped in white linen, laden with food and drink, and up the stone stairs leading to the entrance of Knightsbrook House—her new home. She looked back and saw that he was right. Everyone was distracted…talking, drinking and dancing. No one had noticed their departure. No one would know what they were up to.

He stopped when they entered the house, took both her hands and placed them around his neck, then encircled her waist with his arms.

Rosie's breath caught in her throat in anticipation. She tilted her head back, closed her eyes and parted her lips, waiting for a kiss.

'I know I should wait till our guests leave before doing this, but I've been waiting for so long I can't wait a minute longer.'

Rosie's hammering heart increased its tempo. 'Really? And what might "this" be?' she asked, her voice a breathy whisper.

'This…'

He began twirling, taking Rosie with him. They spun down the entrance hall, Rosie getting dizzier and dizzier. Her laughter joined his as the black and white floor tiles merged into one and the paintings, vases and statues that lined the walls whirled past.

When they reached the staircase they stopped suddenly, but the room continued to spin. He held her tightly, to stop himself from falling and to save her. But neither worked.

They collapsed in a tangled mass of arms and legs at the foot of the stairs.

Rosie continued to giggle—only to have her giggles stifled when his lips found hers. She kissed him back, her heart overflowing with love, passion and deep contentment.

* * * * *

COMING SOON!

We really hope you enjoyed reading this book. If you're looking for more romance, be sure to head to the shops when new books are available on

Thursday 31st October

To see which titles are coming soon, please visit

millsandboon.co.uk/nextmonth

MILLS & BOON

Coming next month

MISS LOTTIE'S CHRISTMAS PROTECTOR
Sophia James

'Are you married, sir?'

'I am not.' Jasper tried to keep the relief from his words.

'But would you want to be? Married, I mean? One day?'

She was observing him as if she were a scientist and he was an undiscovered species. One which might be the answer to an age-old question. One from whom she could obtain useful information about the state of Holy Matrimony.

'It would depend on the woman.' He couldn't remember in his life a more unusual conversation. Was she in the market for a groom or was it for someone else she asked?

'But you are not averse to the idea of it?' She blurted this out. 'If she was the right one?'

Lord, was she proposing to him? Was this some wild joke that would be exposed in the next moment or two? Had the Fairclough family fallen down on their luck and she saw his fortune as some sort of a solution? Thoughts spun quickly, one on top of another and suddenly he'd had enough. 'Where the hell is your brother, Miss Fairclough?'

She looked at him blankly. 'Pardon?'

'Silas. Why is he not here with you and seeing to your needs?'

'You know my brother?'

Her eyes were not quite focused on him, he thought then, and wondered momentarily if she could be using some drug to alter perception. But surely not. The Faircloughs were known near and far for their godly works and charitable ways. It was his own appalling past that was colouring such thoughts.

'I do know him. I employed him once in my engineering firm.'

'Oh, my goodness.' She fumbled then for the bag on the floor in front of her, a decent-sized reticule full of belongings. Finally, she extracted some spectacles. He saw they'd been broken, one arm tied on firmly with a piece of string. When she had them in place her eyes widened in shock.

'It is you.'

'I am afraid so.'

'Hell.'

That sounded neither godly nor saintly and everything he believed of Miss Charlotte Fairclough was again turned upside down.

Continue reading
MISS LOTTIE'S CHRISTMAS PROTECTOR
Sophia James

Available next month
www.millsandboon.co.uk

LET'S TALK
Romance

For exclusive extracts, competitions
and special offers, find us online:

f facebook.com/millsandboon

🐦 @MillsandBoon

📷 @MillsandBoonUK

Get in touch on 01413 063232

For all the latest titles coming soon, visit
millsandboon.co.uk/nextmonth

MILLS & BOON

THE HEART OF ROMANCE

A ROMANCE FOR EVERY KIND OF READER

MODERN

Prepare to be swept off your feet by sophisticated, sexy and seductive heroes, in some of the world's most glamourous and romantic locations, where power and passion collide.
8 stories per month.

HISTORICAL

Escape with historical heroes from time gone by. Whether your passion is for wicked Regency Rakes, muscled Vikings or rugged Highlanders, awaken the romance of the past.
6 stories per month.

MEDICAL

Set your pulse racing with dedicated, delectable doctors in the high-pressure world of medicine, where emotions run high and passion, comfort and love are the best medicine.
6 stories per month.

True Love

Celebrate true love with tender stories of heartfelt romance, fro the rush of falling in love to the joy a new baby can bring, and a focus on the emotional heart of a relationship.
8 stories per month.

Desire

Indulge in secrets and scandal, intense drama and plenty of sizzi hot action with powerful and passionate heroes who have it all: wealth, status, good looks…everything but the right woman.
6 stories per month.

HEROES

Experience all the excitement of a gripping thriller, with an inte romance at its heart. Resourceful, true-to-life women and strong fearless men face danger and desire - a killer combination!
8 stories per month.

DARE

Sensual love stories featuring smart, sassy heroines you'd want as best friend, and compelling intense heroes who are worthy of th
4 stories per month.

To see which titles are coming soon, please visit

millsandboon.co.uk/nextmonth